THE SAVED SEAT

A Story of Hope For Every Fractured Family

"You intended to harm me, but God intended it for good to accomplish what is now being done, the saving of many lives." Genesis 50:20

By Bob Steinkamp

THE SAVED SEAT

ISBN 978-1-892230-25-6

by Robert E. Steinkamp

Rejoice Marriage Ministries, Inc.
Bob and Charlyne Steinkamp, Co-Founders
Post Office Box 10548
Pompano Beach, Florida 33060 USA
(954) 941-6508

www.RejoiceMinistries.org
www.StopDivorceRadio.org
www.StopDivorce.org

Printed in the United States of America

In Appreciation

This book is dedicated to every man and woman who helped to make it possible. Friends of this Ministry proofed the manuscript for us. Others read it for accuracy. Still others contributed toward printing this book, the longest of the 20 books that God has allowed us to write.

The story was written to be an easy read account of what happened to a fictional family when satan attacked them. It was also written to share the only lasting solution to strife within marriage.

Even though the story is fiction, the fact is that today a large percentage of our families are facing the enemy's attack. Many people will read this story to be entertained, but during the process will have God reveal to them the solution for their marriage problems.

We are praying that many hurting spouses will discover the "something" they are searching for is really "Someone," and that His name is Jesus.

He cares for you,
Bob and Charlyne

Chapter 1

Shocked Into Reality

The incessant buzz from the radio's alarm clock could not be stopped by Sam turning over in bed and covering his head with the pillow. Was it really 2 A.M. and time to get up for work? It seemed as though he had only fallen asleep a few minutes ago. From under the pillow Sam's right hand reached out and hit the snooze button.

As Sam Sullivan began to awaken, reality hit him like a brick. Every day his small weekly hotel room seemed to be shrinking and the smell of leftover stale cigarette smoke seemed to be increasing. Sam's physical surroundings would have seemed royal compared to his emotional surroundings. Several months prior, Sam and his wife had separated.

Like every couple, the Sullivans had moments of disagreement. Over time the intensity of their disagreements escalated. Sadly, the three Sullivan children were witness to much of what was happening in their home. One evening during an especially vocal argument, one of the kids, Connie, had called 911 and the dissolving of the Sullivan's once happy family seemed to be under way. As suggested by one of the police officers who had responded that night, Becky Sullivan took the children and went to a hotel.

Sam had found himself alone in their home, which on any other night would be filled with the laughter and the noise of a mom and dad enjoying evening family activities with their children. Once his family had been escorted out of their own home by the police, Sam just sat in a darkened family room, as silent as death and sobbed. He did not care that their neighbors had seen three police cars, with lights and sirens, roar up to their home. It did not matter who saw his family leave. It only mattered that his family was in trouble.

"There must be some help for this," Sam mumbled to himself. "If only I knew where to look, but I don't."

Didn't the Sullivans know about God and the help Jesus can bring to a family when someone calls on Him? Sadly, they did not. The Sullivans only knew of the abstract far away God. Both Sam and Becky acknowledged God as their Creator, but neither had a personal relationship with Him. They attended church with their children on Easter and Christmas.

Each summer the Tomlinsons, their next-door neighbors, would take the children to Vacation Bible School at their church. The kids always enjoyed it, but somehow Sam and Becky always were busy on that special night at the end when parents would come and see what their children had accomplished that week and the parents would also hear about Jesus.

That night, long after things had settled down, Becky sat in a hotel room reading the domestic violence folder that had been given her by one of the police officers. Before then, Becky had never considered herself to be a victim of domestic violence. Sam had never touched her in anger. Looking at her three precious children who had gone through so much that evening, Becky read on in her brochure about how verbal abuse will turn to physical abuse if not checked.

Becky bristled as she read about how necessary it was for her to obtain a protective order against her "abusive" husband. Had their well-intended child not called 911, by now the Sullivans would have made up, the incident forgotten, and they would be asleep in each other's arms. This time things would be far different.

The following morning, while getting three children ready for school wearing the same clothes they had worn the night before and fielding questions such as "When will daddy be here?" Becky attempted to shield both her heartbreak and her fear from her children. After dropping them off at school, Becky visited the courthouse. Something inside her was saying "wrong" every step of the way, but Mrs. Sullivan did as she was instructed and answered the questions with some guidance, making her husband appear to be a man he was not.

"Have you ever feared for your safety?" Becky was asked.

"He has never touched me, but he does yell when he gets mad," Becky replied.

"So your answer would be yes," she was coached.

Half an hour later she walked out of the courthouse with a piece of paper in her hand that said her husband could not come within 1,000 feet of her. Something was just not right about all this, but she was doing what the experts were all telling her to do, "for the sake of your children."

Becky sat in her car outside the courthouse and sobbed as she read the words on her copy of the protective order. The man described on that form was not her husband, but was a monster she did not even know. The order detailed how she could have no contact in person, by phone, by email or any other means for the next 90 days. This meant she could not see, hear or touch her husband for the next three months! Becky broke into violent sobs, not just crying but gut-wrenching sobs.

Becky felt it coming like a huge wave from deep within her belly. All she could do was open the car door and vomit on the street. Her sickness brought relief to her sobs, but not to the heartache.

Half an hour later, still sitting in the same parking place, Becky had regained her composure. She dried her eyes with tissue as best she could, pulled down her window visor to use the mirror and attempted to apply enough cosmetics to make herself presentable. She then went back and attempted to have the now tear-soaked court order revoked.

"Once it is signed by a judge, it is irreversible," the court clerk advised. "It is a court order and you must abide by it. Your attorney can explain it all to you."

"My attorney?" Becky thought. "I don't even have an attorney. What would I need an attorney for? Oh my gosh! They are talking about divorce!"

Becky returned to her car and the sobbing/vomiting resumed. Somehow she managed to drive herself back to the hotel. Once inside, alone and afraid, Becky began to read attorney ads in the Yellow Pages. She was attracted to one advertisement that proclaimed, "We know how you feel."

"If they know how I feel," Becky said aloud, "they can get me out of this nightmare. I only want our family back like it was."

Our Lord Jesus has other plans for the Sullivan family. He wants this precious family back together under one roof, but not like they had been. The Lord wants them loving and serving Him. He would do whatever was needed to bring that about, as both Sam and Becky would discover in the days ahead.

That afternoon Becky asked her friend, Millie, to pick up her children at school so that Becky could keep her 3 P.M. appointment with the attorney who "knows how you feel."

The attorney who "knows how you feel" also thought that he "knows what you need." He explained to Becky that since a protective order was in place, she would need an attorney to communicate with Sam's attorney on things as small as school events. Before she realized it, Becky had signed a stack of papers to "protect you." She had also signed a sizable check for his retainer. Even though it was the last thing she wanted, Becky had just instituted a divorce.

Chapter 2

A Friend In Need

Sitting on the side of his bed staring at the clock did not make it roll back. It was now after 2 A.M. and time for Sam to get up for work. There was no need to shower or shave. In fact, the man who had trained him for his new career said the rougher he looked the easier his job would be. As Sam pulled on a pair of dirty black jeans and an even dirtier black T-shirt, he thought about all the nights at home when he would be getting up at this hour. Only at home, he might check on his children, get a drink of water and slide back into bed beside a soundly sleeping Becky for several more hours of sleep.

"Man, have things changed," he mumbled. Grabbing his cell phone out of its charger, he flipped off the light and headed for the door. After a cup of coffee from the lobby vending machine, and a half hearted hello to the dozing front desk clerk, Sam was on his way across the parking lot. He headed for the small black tow truck parked discreetly in the back of the lot. For the next eight or ten hours our friend Sam would be behind the wheel of that tow truck, attempting to locate and recover cars and small trucks that were being repossessed by banks.

Sam had not been a repo man for very long. In fact he used to be a banker himself, working for the very institution who financed the vehicles he would be searching for early today.

This chapter of Sam's life began a few weeks ago. It actually began on the afternoon following the 911 incident with his wife. Sam was a successful banker, well liked and respected in his community and by his employer, a nationwide banking chain. Part of Sam's work involved watching out for his bank's interest on loans. He frequently worked with process servers from the sheriff's office when it was necessary to serve an eviction or foreclosure notice on the bank financed property. It was also his duty from time to time to arrange for the repossession of a bank financed vehicle.

Sam enjoyed making loans much more than he did calling them in, knowing the heartache it would cause a family. But he also understood his responsibility to the bank to watch out for their monies.

Nothing was unusual that day when Ryan, a well-known process server, walked into Sam's office at the bank. What was unusual was the stern expression on the face of the normally jovial Ryan. Sam did not expect what was about to happen to him.

"Sam," Ryan began, "before you say anything I need to advise you that I am here in an official capacity. This matter concerns you personally and not the bank."

Sam felt the blood drain from his face. He did not know the details, but he knew this was something related to the 911 incident the previous night. Yet, at the same time, even Sam knew how long it often took the bank for their legal paperwork to be processed in the system. What happened next hit Sam like a full force blow from an NFL player directly to his stomach.

"You are being served with an Order of Protection, issued by the court. You are prohibited by law from coming within 1,000 feet of Rebecca Catherine Sullivan. You are also prohibited by law from having any contact with her in person, by email, by phone, by postal mail or by any other means. Doing so could place you in contempt of court and subject you to jail time. You are hereby served at 4:21 P.M. on this date. Your attorney can answer any questions you might have about this order." With that, Ryan uttered, "I'm sorry. I'm just so sorry." He turned and left Sam's office.

Sam literally slumped in his desk chair without even looking at the paper that had been handed to him. As soon as he began to come to his senses as best he could, Sam put his phone on "Do Not Disturb" and closed his door. He stared at the order in his hand in total disbelief. It was a full five minutes before Sam could even comprehend what this all meant.

He had attempted to call home several times that day to apologize to Becky for his actions the night before. Sam had even considered sending her flowers, but then thought they would mean so much more if he carried them home with him at the end of the day. He was certain that a night apart would have cleared the air between his wife and him. In fact, Sam anticipated a good night at home with his family that evening and everything from the previous night being forgotten. But now this...!

Sam felt his pulse race as he read instructions attached to the order on how to call a local police department to stand by while he removed his personal items from their home. The thought of going to his home, not because it was the end of the day, but because it was the end of a marriage, was overwhelming. What items would he take? Where would he take them? What would Becky say? What about his kids? This was all more than Sam could process, so he left work early.

Sam got behind the wheel of his car, unsure of his destination. When his cell phone rang, he was certain it was

Becky telling him what was for dinner and apologizing for her part of the incident the previous night. Sam was so certain who was calling that he did not even look at the caller ID before he answered.

"Sam, you all right buddy? Your secretary said you left in a hurry and were really distressed about something. I'm sorry to call your cell phone, but wanted to see if there was anything I could do. Are you all right?" The caller was Jerry, the owner of the recovery company that the bank used to repossess vehicles. Sam and Jerry had never had more than a business relationship and Sam was surprised to be hearing from him right then. Nevertheless, Sam poured out his heart to Jerry.

It was Jerry who literally walked Sam through the next 24 hours. Jerry was the one who made the call to the Police Department that night when Sam was composed enough to go home to get his clothing. In fact, that trip was made in Jerry's tow truck. Sam was unable to even drive.

During a very emotional move from his home, during which Jerry talked to Becky outdoors while Sam packed his clothing, two police officers stood by. On his last trip from the home, Sam saw a sobbing Becky leaning against a tree.

"I love you, hon. I always will," Sam shouted, only to have his last word interrupted by one of the police officers.

"I'm sorry, sir, you cannot talk to her. If you do it again you'll be in violation of the restraining order, and I'll have to arrest you," the officer warned sternly.

Jerry was about as hard as they come. It is doubtful he had even seen the inside of a church in many years. He could take away a family's only means of transportation without blinking an eye, but the idea of a man not being able to tell his wife that he loved her got under his skin.

"Becky, I don't know what's going on here, but I've spent four hours with your husband and I know beyond any doubt the man loves you. Maybe he can't talk to you temporarily, but I sure can. Take care of yourself and I will take care of your husband. We will get this family back together, I promise you." Seeing Jerry's boldness lifted Sam's spirits enough to enable him to turn his back on a crying wife, dying inside and walk away from his family.

"Sir," the officer aimed at Jerry, "I need to warn you not to inter. . . ."

"Yeah, yeah, I know the drill," Jerry snarled back. "I pull cars for a living. I have had people put baseball bats through my truck window, with me inside. I've had people sic pit bulls on me. I've been shot at more times than I can count. I've had giants jump on my back while I was bent over hooking up their car. So you know what? Your words don't bother me too much. Something is just not right when a man cannot tell his wife he loves her. If I have to go to jail for helping my friend do that, so be it."

Looking at Becky, Jerry almost shouted, "This man loves his wife." The two officers pretended not to hear.

They also acted deaf as Becky exclaimed to the tow truck pulling out of their drive. "Sam, I will always love you too! We'll work this out."

Chapter 3

The Hunter

It was amazing how Jerry stepped in just as Sam needed a friend the most. As happens so often in a crisis, an acquaintance rises to the top and is there just when needed most. Even though neither Jerry nor Sam were Christians, the hand of God was already at work in each of their lives as well as the Sullivan marriage.

Jerry drove Sam to a weekly hotel and got him situated. Even though he had other things to do, Jerry could see Sam's despondent state and did not want to leave him alone.

"We haven't had dinner yet," Jerry said, "so how about letting me buy you a meal?"

"I could not eat a bite," Sam replied, "but to be real honest with you, I do not want to be alone. Could I go along and have coffee?"

"I wouldn't have it any other way."

Five minutes later the two men were in Jerry's tow truck, headed for Denny's. As they rode along, the two men would be in conversation and Sam would forget, just for a split second, the events that had put them together that evening.

Sam made an inquiry about Jerry's recovery business and that opened the door to conversation about something other than family problems and protective orders. As many times as Sam had given Jerry cars to recover when payments were not being made, Sam knew very little about the operation of a repossession tow service.

"I really never gave much thought to what you do," Sam observed. "All I knew was that I could give you vehicle information and somehow you managed to get the car back to the bank. Before tonight I had never even seen your tow truck. I have to tell you when I got up this morning I had no idea I would be out riding with a repo man tonight. After hearing your monologue to that policeman at the house about baseball bats through windshields and people shooting at you, I guess there's a lot more to the story. Am I right?"

Jerry began to explain. "Well, there's a lot more to it than my going to someone's home and saying, 'Hello, I am here to take your car away because you didn't pay for it.' Once in a while that works, but most of the time people make every effort to keep me from getting my hands on their car. My favorites are people who block their cars in with another vehicle or a wall on each end. Did you notice the lift on the back of this truck? I can use it almost like a forklift. I suspect I could get a car out of a locked post office box if I had to," Jerry laughed.

"I look at it as hunting," Jerry continued. "I am the hunter and those cars are the animals. I've got to tell you, after some of the things I've seen, I'm not sure if those cars are the animals or we are the animals. Most of the people I deal with are trying to beat the system, but once in a while I come across a situation where I'm ready to take money out of my own pocket and get their payments caught up."

Even in Sam's despair, he was seeing a new side to Jerry, the repo guy. Sam had fielded a few complaint calls at the bank over how an individual's vehicle had been picked up that had made him wonder if Jerry wasn't the animal in this equation. He could hardly believe his ears, hearing that a repo man was so touched by a family or their situation that he wanted to catch up the payments for them.

"Have you ever actually made payments for people?" Sam inquired.

"I'm not sure how a bank would look at that," Jerry said, "but there have been times when I have handed over more cash to a family than I was making off their repo."

Arriving at Denny's, Sam was surprised that Jerry parked the tow truck in a far corner of the parking lot. "I'm not the most popular guy in town," Jerry volunteered. "A couple times I have come out of places to find my truck tires flattened and a nasty note on the windshield. I can understand how people would take it personally when I haul off their wheels, but I'm only doing what a bank or finance company tells me to do. Besides, if they had been making their payments I would never have met them."

Once inside Denny's, all Sam could notice were couples. Jerry would get his mind off his problems for a minute with talk about his most unusual business, but a thousand and one times Sam would see or hear something that would reopen a very fresh wound; a wound so fresh that he was about to bleed to death. On one hand, Sam appreciated everything Jerry was attempting to do for him, but on the other, he just wanted to go back to his room, crawl under the covers, and maybe, when he woke up, this would all be a bad dream.

Sam decided to order, but even in doing that everything reminded him of Becky. The soup of the day was her favorite. Out of habit, he almost ordered her favorite drink of half iced tea and half water.

Our friend Sam looked around at the people in that restaurant. Not only were they all couples, they all seemed to be happy couples. Where had he and Becky gone wrong? There must be a secret that they had never discovered. Was there any hope now?

The two men sitting in the corner booth made an odd couple. They were contrasts in appearance. One man was short and muscular. He was dressed in dirty black jeans and a T-shirt. His rough hands had grease under the fingernails. His hair was both too long and uncombed. Sitting with him was the composite of a banker. Everything about him from his wing-tipped shoes to his manicured nails said success in business. He still wore the trousers from an expensive suit and a tailored white shirt.

During the time they had been together that afternoon and evening, Jerry had never mentioned a wife. He did not wear a wedding band, nor did he ever mention a family. Sam suspected that if he had been married, some sweet woman would have encouraged him to work on his appearance. Sam was afraid to ask if Jerry was married. Hearing that he had been at one time and that his marriage had ended in divorce would just be too much on this night.

Anyone who watches people would have wondered what the two men had in common because their appearances were so opposite. Only our Lord God could have put those two men together at that time under those circumstances. But that was just the beginning of what God was going to do, not only for those two guys but for two families also.

Chapter 4

"Should We Pray?"

"Here you go, guys," their waitress literally chirped as she came up the aisle with a tray of food. Somehow Sam wished she would just tone down the happy attitude a few degrees. He certainly wasn't happy and was resisting anyone's effort to make his day brighter.

After the traditional "Do you need anything else?" had been delivered and their waitress was on her way to cheer up another table, both men sat with food before them. Jerry made the first comment.

"Ah, do you pray before you eat or anything? I usually don't but I didn't know if you did. Besides, it seems that tonight is the kind of night that somebody should be praying for you guys and I don't know how."

Would you believe that Sam felt the same way? Even though the Lord had no part in his daily life, there comes a time when there's nowhere to turn but to Him, and this was certainly one of those times. However, Jerry had never prayed aloud in his life. Sam had not prayed aloud since childhood. Even so, this odd couple sat awkwardly before their food, refusing to take a bite until someone had prayed.

During a time of crisis, people either turn to God or they turn away from God, often in anger for what He has allowed to happen. There is no room in the theology of the people who turn away from God in anger to take personal responsibility for any of the problem.

The Lord must have been pleased to see those two men

wanting to call on Him, even though neither felt adequate to do so. What they did is what God would want each of His children to do in similar circumstances.

Who do you think would attempt to pray? The roughneck repo guy or the slick and shiny banker? It was the repo guy who made an effort that must have pleased God.

"I guess I could try," Jerry said, "so here goes nothing. *'God, it's me Jerry, the repo guy down here in Fort Lauderdale. It's been a long time since You've heard from me, so I guess everything has been going pretty good, but tonight I am here at Denny's with my friend Sam, the banker. God, You may not know him very well either, but God, tonight we really need Your help. First of all God, I am sorry I haven't talked to You in so long. I know You are there if I need You, but I think You might have wanted more from me. God, thank You for giving us this food. We appreciate it God, but we need something more than food. God, You already know it, but Becky, Sam's wife, has dumped him, and God, we need Your help. God, I can help him get a place to stay the night and I can give him a meal but God, I can't do in his life what needs doing. Only You can do that. God, I don't know how to sign this off to You but I know You've been expecting more from me than I've been giving to You, so this must be the time I start to make things right. God, keep Becky and the kids safe tonight and let Sam not worry about them. I don't know how You do things but God, I'm asking you to solve all this. God, I'm sorry I can't pray very good and we don't talk to one another very much, but thank you God, just for being there and for loving me and for my friend Sam, Amen.'*"

Sam's head remained bowed for several seconds after Jerry had finished praying. When his head came up, Sam's eyes were filled with tears. Was it because of what had happened to him that afternoon, or was it because he had just come before God in prayer for the first time in many years? In truth, it was a combination of both of these plus a third factor. Sam was touched that Jerry had referred to him as a friend in his prayer.

After they finished eating Jerry picked up the tab, touching Sam even more. Once the two men were back in the tow truck, under the cover of darkness, Sam disclosed how much he feared going into that low-price hotel room alone.

"I have an idea," Jerry declared. "Why don't you hang out with me for a few hours? I have a couple cars to grab tonight and you can see how this business works. I may not be the best company in the world, but at least you won't be alone. I can get you back to the hotel when you feel you're ready."

Sam accepted the offer without hesitation. Just 48 hours ago, Sam could not have imagined where he would be tonight. When satan attacks a family, everyone's plans are turned upside down. So often God sends someone like Jerry alongside a hurting and wounded spouse just when they need it the most.

For the next three or four hours Jerry and Sam drove and talked. First they went to Lauderdale Lakes, looking for a car that was not where it was supposed to be. Then they headed north to one of the worst parts of Deerfield Beach, in search of a red pickup truck. When the truck was spotted, Jerry turned off his headlights and quietly got out of the wrecker with a small flashlight to verify the vehicle's VIN number. All of a sudden Sam could understand what Jerry had told him about this being like a hunt. They had found the hunted.

"Everything checks out," Jerry said as he got back behind the wheel of the tow truck. "The rough part is done. Give me a second and we will be on our way." Still with the lights off, Jerry quickly and quietly maneuvered the tow truck behind the pickup. He quickly jumped out. Sam turned his head and watched Jerry work through the rear window of the tow truck. He was amazed at how quickly Jerry moved a couple of levers, extended the lift and had the pickup truck lifted. Jerry was only out of the truck less than 30 seconds.

"Got em," Jerry said softly as he jumped back into the truck. "The hard part is over and we just paid for dinner and then some."

A few blocks away Jerry pulled into a shopping center parking lot where he got out and secured the pickup truck for transport to the impound lot. Back in the truck, he called the non-emergency number of Deerfield Beach police to give them information on the truck he had just repossessed. Sam discovered that many people will report their cars stolen, even when they are months behind on payments. Keeping a repo log saves the police department a lot of time and effort.

"How many of these do you do a night?" Sam inquired.

"Again, it's like hunting. On a good night I'll get a couple or three. Other nights I drive from one end of Broward County to the other and never pull a thing. In the long run it all evens out and me and my guys make a decent living. No one is getting rich, but at least no one is going to repo the repo man's wrecker."

Sam had never been a hunter, but there was something about this job that fascinated him. As it grew later he was even able to forget about his personal problems a bit more. Nevertheless, every few minutes the thought would hit him that he was going home to a hotel room and not to his family. He had been especially burdened when Jerry called the Police

Department to report the repo. Everything seemed so clinical yet this was affecting a real family. Sam wondered if the two police officers who had come to his home earlier that evening, while he moved out, had any emotion at all for what was taking place, namely the start of the death of a family.

After the repossessed pickup truck was secured at the impound lot, Jerry could see that Sam was still greatly dreading walking into that hotel room alone. Most nights Jerry was all alone so he really appreciated Sam's company, such as it was. Every other sentence Sam was talking about his family or questioning his future.

"Too bad you have to work tomorrow," Jerry volunteered. "Otherwise I would say let's stop for coffee and doughnuts, and you could stay with me all night."

"To tell you the truth, I was going to take a personal day tomorrow. I cannot work in the shape I'm in tonight, so if you don't mind, let me tag along with you. If I get good and tired maybe I can sleep tomorrow."

That turned out to be a good night for Jerry. He repossessed three vehicles before dawn. When the last car was found, Sam even got out of the wrecker while it was being hooked up.

"There's a lot more to it, but if you ever need a job, I can find one for you," Jerry joked afterwards. Neither man realized how prophetic those words would be.

Chapter 5

"We Are Restructuring"

For the first few days after that fateful night for the Sullivan family, Sam functioned like a man who had just experienced having the wind knocked out of him. It wasn't the wind, but rather a family that had been knocked out of him.

Sam did take personal time for that first post separation day. His shirts were not pressed nearly as nicely, nor did his ties always match with his suit, but nevertheless Sam was working at the bank every day. There was no wife around to remind him when it was time for a haircut, nor did he start his days with a hug and kiss from the wife of his youth.

A couple weeks after this all began, Sam had confided in the bank's Director of Human Resources what was happening in his life when he changed his mailing address from his home to a post office box. Sam did not suspect that any other individual in his large bank had any idea that he had major marriage problems.

Wanda Eastman had been Sam's secretary for as long as he had been a bank officer. This woman, now in her 50s, had started her career as a bank teller over 20 years before. Wanda was often teased by her coworkers for having a sixth sense about what was happening at the bank. Although not one to gossip, Wanda often seemed to have her ear to the track and to know what was about to happen.

Would you be surprised to learn that Wanda was a Christian? She was not the kind of person to display several Bibles on her desk, nor did she have Scriptures on Post-It notes stuck on her computer. However, if you had opened any of Wanda's desk drawers, these items of faith were quickly available to her. Although Wanda could not be called a prophet, the Holy Spirit often revealed to her people and situations that stood in need of prayer. More than once Wanda had carried a burden to the Lord for a situation that was later both revealed and resolved. Wanda was not surprised when she started to carry a tremendous prayer burden for Sam.

For the past two weeks or so, Wanda had sensed that something horrible was happening in her boss' life. In addition to Sam's less than perfect appearance, and the absence of phone calls from and to Becky, Wanda had observed many times through the glass wall Sam's long and frequent pensive moments. His appearance was not that of a man on the job daydreaming about a new boat or an upcoming vacation. To Wanda, Sam appeared more like a man with a problem to which there is no solution.

The bank was not as concerned with Sam's personal life as they were with his productivity. Since the troubles at home began, Sam had been making almost daily blunders on the job, many of which cost the bank money. In this day's tight economy, even one such mistake would have been one too many in the banking industry. Wanda did a great job of absorbing many of Sam's mistakes. This dear woman did an even better job of praying for him and his family.

Late one Friday afternoon, Wanda looked up from her keyboard to see three people walking toward her desk, with Sam's office directly behind. "Oh my gosh, why do they always do this on Friday afternoons?" she mumbled to herself. Wanda pretended to be typing, but in truth she was in prayer as two of the three walked by her and into Sam's office.

"Sam, I am so sorry," the bank's Vice President said without looking Sam in the eye.

"We are restructuring the bank and your position has been abolished," the Director of Human Resources said as she handed Sam the empty cardboard box she had been carrying.

"We are required to escort you off the property. Here is an envelope with all of your severance information. You're welcome to call the bank's main Human Resources Department for any questions you might have."

The third man in the party, who waited by Wanda's desk, was a bank security guard, but he would not be needed at this termination. Any self-esteem, any gleam of hope, any zeal for life Sam Sullivan possessed had just been vaporized. First he lost his family; now he was losing his career. Sam slumped in his desk chair and looked at the windows in his office, wishing he could force them open and jump onto Broward Boulevard far below.

The Human Resources Director allowed Sam a full two minutes to grasp what was happening before she spoke. "Sam, I know this is rough, but you know what the economy is like. The bank has had to make some hard decisions. I regret that you became a victim of one of those decisions."

Sam only comprehended about every other word the lady was saying to him. All he knew was that he lost his family and now he lost his job. What more could happen?

Wanda sat at her desk and pretended not to notice what was happening in the glass cubicle directly behind her. Tears filled her eyes, not because the man was being fired, but because she sensed something was very wrong in Sam's life. *"God, please help. Help them right now in the name of Jesus.*

Amen."

In the next half hour, years of Sam's banking career were packed into a single cardboard box. The plaques came off the wall. When the Human Resources Director picked up Sam's nameplate from his desk and put it into the box, he almost laughed. Why would he ever need that?

Finally the moment came that Wanda had been dreading. With the security guard leading the way with the box of Sam's personal items, and the Human Resources Director following Sam, the short procession started for the employee's entrance. By now, word of what was happening had spread to the entire floor. Sam paused by Wanda's desk long enough for them to exchange a tearful hug and goodbye.

"Mr. Sullivan, I will be praying for you. We don't know what it is, but God has a plan and a purpose in all of this. He will get the glory if you will allow Him to," Wanda tearfully expressed. She had witnessed scenes like this too often down through the years. Now it seemed that almost every Friday afternoon someone else was being terminated. She had been working at this bank since most of the other employees were still in diapers. Maybe it was time for her to retire.

Sam's reply cancelled out any potential retirement plans Wanda might be entertaining. "Please pray for me and for my family, Wanda. Whatever it is in you that I have seen day after day, I want some."

At one time she would have been embarrassed for the Director of Human Resources and a security guard to have heard the statement of faith that she had just proclaimed to Sam Sullivan, but right then the broken heart of a man who had been a good boss, but who was walking out of her life without Christ, meant more to Wanda than did her job.

The security guard carried Sam's box of personal effects all the way to his car. Sam got behind the wheel as the man slid the box into the back seat. Reaching through the open driver's window the guard placed his hand on Sam's shoulder for what seemed like the longest time. Along with Wanda's faith-filled comments as he left his office for the final time, the reassurance of that guard's touch spoke care and compassion to Sam's broken spirit.

Sam sat in that parking lot for the longest time, not even bothering to start his car. He was perspiring in the hot Florida weather but seemed to not even notice. Sam looked up at the bank building window where his office had been until about 45 minutes before.

"How do you drive away from something knowing you'll never be there again?" Sam asked himself aloud.

Finally Sam started his car and merged out into the busy Andrews Avenue traffic. Out of habit after so many years, Sam started north to his family home, not west to his hotel. As he crossed Sunrise Boulevard, Sam remembered his family situation and the protective order. The tears that had been under control for a few minutes started all over again. Sam pulled into a parking lot and wept and wept and wept.

As Sam regained his composure, the fear set in. He was unemployed! His wife was divorcing him! He lived in a hotel! He owed alimony and child support! What if he got sick? He had even lost his Blackberry when he left the bank. Anyone passing by who looked at the car sitting sideways in the parking lot of that shopping center would have thought that the driver was having a seizure as Sam cried until he shook.

Sam Sullivan certainly was not the only employee being

terminated that Friday afternoon. Sadly, he was not the only man or woman living in a hotel, with divorce threatening his family. In fact, he probably was not the only axed employee that day who also faced divorce. In fact, many of the men and women going through the same situation as Sam, had a Friend Who is above all friends. His name is Jesus. He promises to walk with us through every battle we face. That Friend can make such a difference. We can only pray that someone soon introduces Sam to Jesus Christ, telling how Jesus died on the cross for our sins, not only to give us life eternal, but to help us, to be with us, to comfort us in this life. That, my friend, is what Sam is seeking - but he doesn't know it.

Once in his hotel room, still wearing his banker's suit, Sam fell face down on his bed. Hours later he awoke to a ringing telephone in a darkened room. For a moment he did not know where he was and could not remember his circumstances, but before he found the light switch and the phone his sad circumstances were re-orientated in his mind. He managed to knock the phone off the bedside table and then attempted to speak into the wrong end before mumbling in a deep tone what could have been something like "Hello."

"Sam, it's Jerry. Are you all right? You sound terrible." In recent weeks Sam the banker and Jerry the repo guy had become friends. They usually had dinner together several nights a week and Sam had ridden along with Jerry one night each weekend since the separation. Even with all the time they spent together, Sam still knew very little about Jerry.

"Wanda called me as soon as she got home this evening and told me what happened today. I am so, so sorry. What can I do to help you right now?"

"I don't even know," Sam, now a former banker, replied. "Tailspin is not even the word for where I am right now. No job, no family, no future, no hope. Jerry, I know your intentions are great, but there's nothing that you can do."

"Remember that night a few weeks ago when you were given a restraining order and you sounded about like this? Remember what we did? Take off that banker's suit buddy, 'cause I'm coming to pick you up and we're going hunting tonight, Fort Lauderdale style."

"No.., no, I cannot impose on you again. It seems like your work is all gloom and doom without my sunshine in your truck. Thanks, but I just couldn't do that again. It's asking too much of you." Sam's voice was hardly recognizable as his own, he was so distraught.

"There's a chapter to the Jerry story that you've never heard, Sam. I will be downstairs to pick you up in about 15 minutes. Unless the 'hunting' is great tonight, I'll have time to share with you."

Exactly 15 minutes later Sam exited the elevator from the hotel to see the black tow truck waiting for him. He wore a pair of jeans, sneakers, and a sweatshirt, none of which had seen the laundry for a while.

"Well," Jerry began, "I finally got you looking like a repo guy." Red, swollen eyes resulting from hours of crying only added to his unkept appearance.

Dinner for the odd couple that night consisted of a bag of burgers while sitting in the tow truck parked in the lot at Krystal Hamburgers on Sunrise Boulevard. The darkness of the cab of that truck was about to serve as a confessional for two men, both of whom hurt very deeply.

Chapter 6

"My Wife Is Crazy!"

"It don't matter what's wrong, a bag of square hamburgers always helps," Jerry exclaimed as he popped an entire small square burger into his mouth. He tossed its cardboard container onto the dashboard to join half a dozen others already there. The sweet smell of steamed onions filled the cab.

Sam sipped on coffee from a Styrofoam cup, saying very little. His stomach was too unsettled to eat a thing.

"What are you going to do?" Jerry asked. "Got any idea?"

"I am still in shock," Sam replied. I can't believe where this marriage mess has taken me, and on top of it, I get fired! You know, when I think about it, it's all Becky's fault that I got fired. If I was still living at home I probably could've done my job and no one would've singled me out for the axe. You know what she did today? She killed her hopes for child support and alimony. She wants to drain me yet at the same time make it impossible for me to keep a job."

Jerry might be just the repo guy, but he's people smart. He could tell Sam was near the boiling point. "We hang out together a lot, but you don't really know me, do you, Sam?"

"What is there to know? You have a repo business, work hard, and are a likable guy. That's about the size of it. Is there something else I need to know? Are you an axe murderer or something?"

"No, nothing like that," Jerry laughed. "But about five years ago I was sitting on that side of the truck where you are now, if you get my meaning. And no, I was not a banker."

"You mean...?" Sam questioned.

"Yes sir, I'm sorry to say that I've got a failed marriage under my belt. I'm not proud of what happened, but I'm going on as best I can."

"I've often wondered about your past," Sam interjected. "I thought you might have been in jail or something."

"A little of that also, but there's a lot more to it. Do you want to hear my story? I don't tell this often, but I think that tonight you need to hear that you can go through a divorce and survive."

Jerry popped the final square burger into his mouth, tossed a ketchup packet out the window, and yet another cardboard container onto the dashboard, all in one motion. It was evident he was getting ready to tell quite a story. After one quick slurp from the straw, Jerry began.

"I met Kathy during my first year of college at Mississippi State," Jerry began.

Sam quickly interrupted, "You mean you went to... college?"

"Yeah, I know. I don't look like college material now, but that's part of our story. Anyhow, I met Kathy during my first year of college and brought her to Lauderdale for spring break. It was love at first sight between her and me. I guess it was also love at first sight for Fort Lauderdale. Like so many spring breakers do, I made up my mind right then that some day I would live here.

"Anyhow, Kathy got pregnant and we got married, but I don't know which happened first. I dropped out of college at the end of the first year, thinking that's what it would take to support a wife and kid. By the way, you know how to make a woman stop being attractive to you?"

"No, I guess I really don't," Sam answered. He was uncomfortable with where Jerry was going. This was not the night Sam wanted to hear anti-marriage jokes.

"You marry her," Jerry howled. As soon as he said it, Jerry knew he had just put his foot in his mouth. Sam understood his friend was just trying to lighten up a heavy topic in the only way he knew how, making a joke.

"Back to my story," Jerry continued. "Nine months later we had Jerry Junior. He was a trip. We had moved to Mobile, Alabama so Kathy could be near her parents. I got a job at a gas station that had a pretty busy wrecker's service. I guess that's where the repo thing really started. Once in a while a bank in Mobile would call us to pick up a car for them. I got to be pretty good at locating cars no on else could find.

"Unfortunately, while I was out looking for repos, my wife needed a husband. She became friends with a couple who lived in our apartment building. It breaks my heart to say it, but that husband treated my wife better than I did. Long story short is that he ended up divorcing his wife. Kathy divorced me, took Junior and they moved to I don't know where."

"Sam, man I know what you're going through. I was mad. I was hurt. I was crazy. I was out of my mind. You asked if I had been in jail. Yes, during the same time. I wanted to talk to the guy that took away my wife and it got out of control. He went to the hospital, but I went to jail.

"I know what it's like to feel so helpless, like everything is moving around you and there is nothing you can do about it. I thought I would never see Junior again. By the way, he's now 11 years old and comes to see me two weeks every summer. It's not the same as being with him all the time, but we do have a blast while he is here. You won't have a seat over there when the son comes to town. He thinks he has about the coolest dad around because of what I do.

"Kathy, now that's another story. My wife is crazy. I tell you, she is certifiably crazy. I try not to talk to her, except about Junior. The guy she took off with went back to his own wife pretty quick. Now, why she would take him back I'll never know, but she did. For a couple of years Kathy has been on this kick that I'm coming back to her, which will never happen."

Sam lost a bit of Jerry's story at this point. He was trying to imagine Becky calling him and asking him to come home and how quick he would be there.

"...and Kathy says that now she's doing something called 'standing' and asking God to bring me home. Sounds like witchcraft to me. She probably has a doll that looks like me sitting in a toy tow truck that she sticks pins in," Jerry laughed.

"I have to admit that she sounds different when I talk to her, but I'm sure that's just part of her act. From what Junior tells me, she even got religion. When he was down here last summer the first meal we ate together, the food came, and the kid bowed his head and prayed out loud. I mean there's nothing wrong with that, and I'm glad she's raising him right but if it's all just a ploy to get me to come back to Alabama, buddy, it ain't gonna work.

"It doesn't matter how many times she tells me she's forgiven me and how many times she asks me to forgive her, I'm not falling for her tricks. I know if I went back it would be the same story, different day.

"One week I forgot to send my child support check to Kathy. You would not believe the stuff I got when I called her. She's going on, 'That's all right honey, I forgive you,' and this stuff about God being her Provider and not me. Man, oh man, not only is she crazy, she's trying to drive me crazy.

"There is just one fly in the ointment, though. Who had the affair? I think that Bible she talks about all the time calls that adultery. She and I kind of got into it on the phone one night over that, and she's telling me how God has forgiven her and she's asking me to forgive her. I just don't get it. Now let me tell you, I haven't been a good boy all the time, but I'm not trying to say I am a child of God either."

Sam was amazed at how a man who had been so closed about his past could now be so open. Sam thought back a few weeks to that night he was forced from his home. When he and Jerry sat in Denny's at Commercial and Federal and Jerry had prayed, Sam sensed that Jerry had heard someone pray like he was praying. It must have been Jerry's own son. Sam thought how proud he would be to hear one of his sons, Grant or Ryan, praying aloud.

Jerry continued on with the story, but Sam's thoughts had wandered. At first he was thinking of one of his sons praying, and how great it would be if Becky would catch on to religion like Jerry's wife had. Sam wondered if that should happen, would he ever be invited home?

Later on in his monologue, Jerry revealed that he had a live-in girlfriend, Anita, and they were planning to get married soon. Jerry had met her when he repossessed her car, and they had clicked. The two of them now live in Anita's small Lauderhill apartment.

"If Kathy would only come to reality that I have another woman now and I have a good life down here, and she would stop calling me a prodigal. She needs to realize I ain't coming home and get on with her life. I am sure getting on with mine and Kathy is not part of that plan. Now let's go do some hunting, Fort Lauderdale style," Jerry wound up.

Chapter 7

The Road to Recovery

Sam had scores of friends, both professional and personal. Many of his professional friends worked at the same bank as he used to, and Sam knew how hesitant employees were to fraternize with discharged employees. The bank strongly frowned upon it and regardless of how close the friendship had been, no one wanted to put their own career at risk. In today's economy, there were more bankers going out the door than coming in.

Many of Sam's other friends had been neighbors. Not a one of the men had contacted him at the bank since that fateful night at home. Sam could only imagine what they must be hearing about him from Becky, which by the way was not the case. Becky had nothing but praise for the kind of husband and father that Sam had been. She wanted and needed her mate back as much as did Sam. Unfortunately, the system had become involved and now a husband and a wife could not even communicate with each other directly, even though both greatly desired to do so.

Once Jerry had disclosed the story, there was no stopping him. Driving south on I-95 into Hollywood, Sam wished he was back in his hotel room alone crying with a broken heart.

"Jerry's Jabber," Sam thought. "Maybe he should change the name of his business to Jerry's Jabber." Somehow Jerry's constant monologue about how bad his wife had been and about how he never wanted to see her again, much less be married to her again, was eating into Sam's spirit. How he wished that Becky could and would invite him home.

Sam tuned out Jerry's jabber by staring out the side window of the tow truck. It seemed as though every car they passed was occupied by a man and a woman, on their way home from an evening out together. Even though it was too dark to see the faces of the occupants of the vehicles passing beside them, Sam imagined the couples to all be happy. If Sam could have talked with them, he would have discovered about 50% of them had problems just like he and Becky.

It is satan's lie to convince us that our problems are exclusive to our family. The evil one uses the same tactics in his attempt to bring down every family. What Sam did not know was that Jesus Christ has the answer for every problem that he or his family would ever face. If only Sam knew how to call on Him.

All of the banks recovered their own vehicles whenever possible. Jerry only received the hard-core cases, where vehicles were being hidden or someone was refusing to turn them over. As a result, he was working with only uncooperative people. He ended up in some tight situations, as he and Sam were about to experience on that Friday night.

Exiting at Sheridan Street, Jerry headed the tow truck west to a shopping center, where the bank had heard a vehicle they needed to repossess could be found. For a few minutes Sam forgot all about his problems as they drove up and down lanes of the shopping center's parking lot. Sam's heart raced as much as if he had actually been hunting and was on the trail of an animal.

All of a sudden Jerry hit the brakes hard and turned out the truck's lights. The car had been spotted. As Jerry backed up to it, a man about 20 years old could be seen running out of a pizza shop and directly toward them. In his hand he carried a pizza cutter. Sam, who had been standing beside the tow truck, shouted a word of warning at Jerry.

"Nothing stops me now buddy. This car is mine and I'm not walking away from it," Jerry shouted as he began to work even faster at lifting the repossessed vehicle. "I can't make a living being a wimp and running from thugs."

Sam stood motionless between the fast approaching man, waving the pizza cutter and screaming and Jerry, working feverishly to get the car before the man arrived. Sam wanted to protect his friend, but he stood motionless because he was frozen with fear. Once or twice in his years of banking Sam had seen a customer become that volatile, but that was within a bank and neither one had been carrying a pizza cutter.

For some reason the approaching man came to Sam instead of to Jerry. The tow truck's motor grunted and the car creaked as it was being lifted. The disgruntled man stopped right in Sam's face, but his violent outburst of words continued.

Sam has yet to know exactly how he did it, but somehow he talked the man down. His years of banking experience and talking with customers was put to good use. Two minutes later the man was apologizing and shaking hands with both Sam and Jerry. He voluntarily handed over the keys. Sam had given him tips on the easiest way to get his car back. That man thought he was talking to a repo guy. He never would've suspected he was dealing with a banker, dressed in grubs and helping to tow a car late on Friday night.

"Who-hoo!" Jerry exclaimed as the complacent man went back into the pizza shop. "Man, do you ever have a knack for this business. I usually end up fighting guys like that off and calling the police. How did you do that Sam?"

"I don't know," Sam replied. "I guess I just treated him like I would want to be treated if I was in that situation. Probably won't be too long before I am in that situation, working at a pizza parlor and fighting off the repo man. After all, I'm unemployed, no permanent home, and the courts say I can't go near my family. I really think I know how that guy felt."

Sam's fear that had turned to elation over defusing a bad situation suddenly turned back into despair. It was not unusual these days for Sam's emotions to take wide swings like that. This may be part of the reason that he was terminated at the bank earlier that day.

You could see by looking at Jerry's face that he was thinking something. Finally he spoke. "I have an idea. It probably wouldn't work, but here goes. What do you think about coming to work for me? Most of our work is at night so that would leave your days free for job interviews or to go to court."

Part of that sounded interesting, but the part about going to court knocked the fragile props out from under Sam once again. He had never considered their marriage problems would go so far that he would end up in court against his wife. For the second time today, Sam sat stunned by what he had just heard. He could not even envision being in a courtroom with his wife on the opposite side.

"Well, what do you think? Would you be interested? I know it's a big drop from a banker to a repo man, but it's something to keep your time and your mind occupied. You know that's an important part of this divorce thing – keeping your mind so busy and staying so tired you can't even think about what's really happening.

"There are a couple of state licenses you would need," Jerry continued, "and an internship is involved, but I just think you would make one heck of a repo man. When we combine what I know with what you know, we might even end up partners some day. Interested?"

For some strange reason Sam said that he was. He did not find the idea of men chasing him with pizza cutters to be appealing, but disarming that volatile situation that evening did a lot of good for Sam's self-esteem.

Before the pizza man's car had been inventoried and photographed, as required by law, Jerry and Sam had reached an agreement regarding Sam's employment. Unlike most people who would be looking for a job with the repo company, Sam was confident that his severance package from the bank would cover his financial needs for several months. His objective was simply to stay busy.

Actually, staying busy was Sam's secondary objective. What he desired to accomplish above all else in the world was to see his family back together again with all five of them happy like they used to be. Sam did not know how to even start to accomplish that worthy goal. He had a very limited spiritual frame of reference and had no personal relationship with Jesus Christ.

Before Sam was dropped off at his hotel in the early hours of Saturday morning, Jerry had given him a cell phone. Although far different then the Blackberry he had to turn in on Friday afternoon when he left the bank, the cell phone still gave him a sense of being connected to the outside world.

"Sleep well, buddy," Jerry shouted as Sam exited the tow truck. "Remember, you're on the road to recovery, not only on the road to becoming a recovery specialist, but on the road to recovery in your personal life. Soon Becky will be nothing but a memory to you. There is somebody even better for you! Just wait and see!"

"Nothing but a memory?" Sam fumed as he crossed the hotel lobby. "Somebody better?" Maybe that guy has been through a divorce, but it certainly wasn't from a woman like Becky. Those memories just do not go away.

Sam was physically exhausted and emotionally drained as he entered his darkened hotel room. After a long shower, Sam literally collapsed into bed, where he would sleep for almost 24 hours.

Chapter 8

"You are In My Seat"

Did you ever notice how the sun seems to shine brighter on Sunday than on any other day? Those first rays of the Sunday sun were breaking around the drapes into Sam's hotel room. As happened so often, both before and after, it took Sam a few seconds before the horrible truth hit him.

Each time he awoke and realized he was in a hotel room by himself, forced by law from his own home, he lost his strength. After lying in bed a few more minutes, Sam's feet hit the floor. This Sunday morning was especially difficult when Sam remembered he had lost his job on Friday afternoon. Sam had never felt more alone in his life than he did right then.

What does a person do when they wake up facing the circumstances that Sam had? What was he to do all day to keep his sanity? What would he do on Monday and then on Tuesday and on every day? It seemed he had no purpose in life.

Despondent was not the word to describe Sam's frame of mind alone in that hotel room on that Sunday morning. He showered and shaved as though he actually had somewhere to go. Breakfast that morning was a cup of coffee made in his room and a stale doughnut from last Friday morning.

Sam turned on the television, planning to watch one of the Sunday morning news shows. Instead, the television came on to a church service.

"And that's just what I need," Sam said aloud to no one,

"some preacher shoving a bunch of guilt at me. How does he know what I'm going through or how I feel?"

Yes, Sam, you may not realize it now, but that is exactly what you need. It's not something; it is Someone and His name is Jesus.

Sam sat on the edge of his bed drinking cold coffee and eating a very stale doughnut. He would tell you he was too tired to get up to get the remote control from across the room to change channels, but we know better. God had a claim on Sam's life that Sam did not even realize.

"... and no matter what your circumstances, no matter how big your mountain, nor how deep the valley that you're in right now, Jesus is the answer." Sam was certain that television pastor was staring directly at him as he said, "Will today be the day that you stop trying and start trusting? Jesus is waiting."

Sam stared down at the worn carpet under his feet. He was unable to look the television pastor in the face.

"It does not matter where you are right now," the pastor continued. "You could be in a bar, in jail, or in a hotel room at your wit's end. Jesus is waiting." What he had just heard hit home a little too close for Sam. He got up, walked across the room, found the remote control and turned off the television. Sam returned to the same spot on the edge of the bed and resumed staring at the same tattered carpet.

If there ever was a person the Holy Spirit was dealing with, it was Sam Sullivan on that Sunday morning. Our friend Sam had not gone far enough down hill to listen. He did sit there and think. He thought about that night at Denny's when Jerry had prayed. He thought about hearing of

Jerry's son, Junior, and how bold he was in his faith. He thought about Jerry's wife, praying for her husband to come home when she saw no evidence of that ever happening. Sam thought about his own wife, Becky, who was not around to help him through the crisis of being terminated at the bank. Sam thought about how foolish it was to even consider being a repo man, going from near the top of the financial world feeding chain to near the bottom. Sam sat there and he thought and he sought. Where could he find the answers to all of the problems that faced him?

With an air of determination about him, Sam got up, rummaged through the suits hanging in the small hotel room closet, and quickly selected one. He found a tie that nearly matched, a fairly clean white shirt, and began to get dressed. In 15 minutes it looked as though Sam was ready for a day at the bank. Sam exited the hotel lobby and for a few seconds forgot where he had parked his car when he came in Friday after being fired.

"There has to be one around here somewhere," Sam mumbled as he pulled out of the parking lot way too fast. His eyes scanned left and right looking for a church. Denomination and size did not matter. Sam was looking for relief and today, praise God, he was looking in the right place. He had been moved to find a church.

A few blocks ahead on the left side, Sam spotted a parking lot with about 50 cars in it. As he drove closer, he saw the sign. Sam could not tell you a thing that sign proclaimed, except for the slogan, "You will only be a visitor here once."

Sam's car was a good bit more expensive than every other car parked at that church. As he got out, three or four men standing by the front door looked at him. In fact, they stared at him. Sam walked directly by them as he entered the front door of the church.

Sam uttered a weak "Good morning" as he passed the men. In return, one man basically grunted and a second nodded his head just a bit. Sam's first impression was that he had intruded.

An usher standing inside the door handed Sam a bulletin. The usher never missed a word in his conversation with another usher about how they were going to run off their pastor.

"At least banks have a little class and give you a cardboard box when they're done with you," Sam thought. "Churches must be a tough place."

As shameful as it might be, Sam Sullivan, one of God's hurting children, was looking for relief and answers and was discovering that some churches can be a tough place to visit, as well. No one seemed to care that a lost sinner, on his way to Hell, had just entered their doors looking for answers. God was giving that small congregation an opportunity to lead a man to the Savior. How would they respond? Would Sam's second impression be better than his first?

Sam took a seat on the end of the last pew. By now, he was aware that many people were staring at him. It was almost as though he had walked into someone's living room where he did not belong. Sam saw a man he assumed was the pastor. Wearing a suit and with a Bible in his hand, the man went from pew to pew greeting worshipers. He seemed to have something funny to say to everyone. Although a different man and a different church, Sam was hoping to meet someone like the pastor he had seen on television that morning. Somehow the pastor at this church avoided walking by Sam's pew.

"Excuse me, but you seem to be sitting on our pew," the woman standing in the aisle said, towering over Sam.

Sam was too floored to even reply. He had heard about things like this happening, but he always thought they were a joke. Sam stood and quickly moved out of the pew.

"I'm sorry, but our family has sat on this back pew every Sunday morning for over 50 years," the woman explained. "It would be just too confusing to have our family scattered everywhere."

Sam replied to her comment in a tone equal to the woman's, "Now we couldn't have that happen, could we?"

"You're welcome to use our pew on Sunday night because we don't come to church then."

Sam moved ahead one pew. As totally rejected as he was feeling right then, he wanted to see what this woman's family must be like.

The motto Sam had read on the church sign took on a meaning far different than what was intended: "You'll only be a visitor here once."

Do you realize that Sam had been rejected by his wife and family, rejected by an employer only two days prior, and now he sensed that he was being rejected by a church, just when he needed them the most?

With some confusion, the church service finally started 10 minutes late. A man came to the pulpit and gave announcements along with a few jokes. Sam never realized that church was supposed to be a funny place. Being the banker that he was, Sam counted people. There were 82 souls present that morning in a building that could have accommodated at least 350.

Everyone seemed to know everyone, except for Sam. He heard announcements like, *"If you're interested in attending give Joel a call."* Sam wondered if he had been interested how he would know who Joel was, much less know his phone number.

The unknown man making announcements also recited a prayer list that sounded like he was auctioning. Sam did not know one person could talk so fast. He also wondered how he could have someone pray for him. He needed a real job, not just to be a repo man. Far greater than that, Sam desperately needed his family back together. He was willing to eat beans and drive a tow truck forever, if only his family were together.

After the announcement guy had finished auctioning off the prayer requests, another man stood to lead the music. It might be more accurate to say the second man stood and sang. He announced songs, but that entire church seemed to have laryngitis. On television Sam had seen the people singing joyously, but here everything sounded like a funeral dirge. On top of that, no one smiled, but everyone seemed to be looking at Sam to see what he would do.

Between two of the songs the music guy had everyone shake hands and welcome people around them. Sam suspected that was a code to shake hands with other members of the church, because no one greeted him at all. He turned around to the pew commander's husband behind him, but he was busy making lunch plans with another man.

Right then Sam recalled his early days in banking years before at a small bank in Wilton Manors. The bank president was emphatic that every customer be made to feel welcome, even to the extent of learning and repeating their names. Even though not yet a Christian, our friend Sam reasoned correctly that small churches become big churches like the one he'd seen on television because of the way they treat people.

After half an hour of spiritual gymnastics, the man who Sam had assumed to be the pastor got up to preach. It was not surprising that he began with jokes, a couple at the expense of people in the church. No doubt Fred, whoever he was, had a complex about being short without his pastor joking about it from the pulpit on a Sunday morning.

When the enemy starts things going wrong, it often continues. Would you believe the sermon that day was about tithing? Not only that, the pastor was not well prepared. He cited several economic figures that Sam knew were totally incorrect.

In spite of all that happened to come against him that morning at church, if the Gospel invitation had been given like Sam had seen on television, he probably would have responded and someone could have led him to Christ in a prayer room. Instead the pastor of this church, whose name Sam never heard, apologized to the congregation for having to leave out the back door to meet someone for lunch.

Sam walked out of that service shoulder to shoulder with the other worshipers, none of whom even shook his hand or said hello. Once outside, Sam saw the same four men standing at about the same position. "You guys have a nice afternoon now," Sam delivered with a big smile as he passed them. No one responded. Sam Sullivan determined on that day there was no help for him in the church.

"You will only be a visitor here once." There are hurting people all around us yet we allow lost people to come and go through our churches and we never share the good news of the Gospel of Jesus Christ with them. Not only do we fail to share the Gospel, we fail to show the Gospel to the lost.

Chapter 9

Back on the Home Front

Although Sam Sullivan had no way of knowing it, his wife Becky's life for the months since the 911 incident had been almost as much of a disaster as had his. Becky regretted the 90-day restraining order against Sam from the moment it was handed to her. Her legal problems seemed to be increasing day by day. All she wanted was an opportunity to see her husband, to sit down with him and work out their problems. She knew they could do it just like they had scores of times before.

One of the papers Becky had signed that afternoon was for a restraining order measured not in days but by years. She had instituted a divorce, but they had not been to court. Almost weekly, if not more often, she would receive either a stack of papers from her attorney, (and how she hated that term "my attorney") or a certified letter from the attorney representing Sam. Becky felt completely out of control with the entire situation.

Becky once explained to her neighbor, Mrs. Tomlinson, "I feel like I am on a reverse assembly line. Instead of starting with raw material and ending with a beautiful product, the legal system started with a beautiful family and is attempting to remove something from us at every stop along the judicial way, until there will be nothing left."

A large part of Becky's problems were with her three children. Connie, age 10, was the one who made the 911 call out of fear when her parents were fighting. She was now taking personal responsibility for everything that happened between her parents. Becky attempted to shield her from so much of what was going on because of her guilt.

Becky had taken Connie to a psychologist for two or three visits. Connie was unhappy about going and Becky was unhappy with what was being said there, so the visits ended. Becky was especially concerned that Connie was attempting to dress provocatively, far beyond her years.

Grant, age 12, the Sullivan's oldest son, did as so many oldest sons do in fractured homes. He took it upon himself to be the man of the house. In some ways this was good, such as taking out the garbage for his mom which he had never done before. There was a problem in that Grant would attempt to discipline Ryan, his seven-year-old brother. On top of everything else, Grant was furious with his father for the situation their family was in.

Young Ryan pretended that nothing bothered him. "I like it better when daddy's not here with you two fighting all the time," he had told his mother more than once. At the same time, he was having behavior problems at school. He would get frustrated with his second grade homework and throw temper tantrums, adding to Becky's already overwhelming guilt. Grant would attempt to step into the situation and a family free-for-all would erupt, even without Sam being in the home.

If you can imagine a fractured family without much of a spiritual frame of reference, you had the Sullivans. There were no prayers at meal time, no trips to the Christian bookstore for help, no church services to encourage this family. It is doubtful there was even a Bible in the home. There was no church family to look to for support. There was no pastor to talk with for a word of support on their darkest days. The Sullivan kids were denied the benefit of a youth pastor to look to as a role model.

This family had always been good people, but up until this crisis started, they had been pretty well spiritually self-supporting. In other words, if they did all right for themselves why would they need God? There had never been a major illness in the family. Both Sam and Becky's parents were alive and in reasonably good health. As you can imagine, being a banker, there were no real financial strains. The three Sullivan children got into the normal scrapes for their ages, but they were really pretty great kids, not causing their parents any trouble.

Susan and Doug Tomlinson had been the Sullivan's next-door neighbors at their Coral Ridge home for about 10 years. Doug Tomlinson owned a prominent Fort Lauderdale insurance agency. Although their wives were the best of friends, Sam and Doug had more of a "just wave" type of friendship. Both men worked long hours and did not have the time to socialize like their wives enjoyed. The Tomlinson's children were away at college, so Susan enjoyed spending time with the Sullivan gang. She frequently had them over after school for treats.

Susan and Becky had developed a friendship where they could confide in each other about anything. Many a morning they spent in one of the two kitchens, drinking coffee, and sharing concerns as good friends often do.

Becky had told Susan about some of the strife in their home, although Susan was aware something was not right even before that. One evening while taking out the trash, Susan had heard a rather volatile argument between thc Sullivans.

In the few months that Sam had been gone from the home, the three Sullivan children had developed new, closer relationships with Susan. Many days one of them would be at the Tomlinson home under some pretense, and would find an opportunity to share with Susan about their feelings and their fears.

It is not easy at best to have a father suddenly vanish from home, and things to be so complex that it is difficult to even see him. It is a tragedy that any child would have to go through marital discord without knowing their Heavenly Father loves them and would never leave them. How regrettable that Susan Tomlinson did not herself have a close, personal relationship with Jesus Christ so that she could share His love with those three hurting children.

One evening the Tomlinsons were discussing their friends and neighbors who had such a problem. "You don't get it, do you?" Doug asked. "The guy has a girlfriend. Men don't up and leave home over an argument. He probably got canned from the bank because the girl worked there and is threatening a sexual harassment suit. I have to watch out for it every day with our employees at the insurance agency. It happens all the time."

"Becky has assured me there's no one else involved, Susan replied. "I know Sam and he's just not that kind of guy. His two priorities were his family and his career, whichever came first, and there was no room in his life for anything else."

"Maybe it's her," Doug challenged. "Maybe she's the one with the boyfriend. Maybe she's causing all this and he is the innocent party."

"Douglas, Douglas, Douglas," Susan retorted, "why do you men always think dirty about everything? There's more to life than sex. I can assure you another man is the last thing on Becky's mind right now. She's struggling to survive emotionally and to raise her kids with some degree of normalcy, and you picture her out having an affair. You should be ashamed of yourself!"

Doug Tomlinson raised the magazine he had been reading. To Susan or to anyone else who might have seen him, he appeared to be reading, but deep in his spirit Doug was asking how this tornado of divorce could be headed straight for his neighbor's home. Even more so, Doug placed himself in Sam's shoes and wondered how he could prevent the same thing from happening to his own marriage.

Much like every couple, the Tomlinsons had their moments of disagreement. In about 15 seconds, Doug's mind went through a scenario of he and Susan having a disagreement, of being overheard by the kid next door with the fast 911 finger, of the process starting that was underway right next door to them. Doug shuddered as he thought about himself, being prevented by law from seeing his wife, Susan. He could only envision himself looking gaunt and aged as had happened to Sam in only weeks. The sofa in his office did not sound appealing as a new home.

"Honey," Doug mused, "how do we prevent what's happening next door from happening over here?"

"I do not know," Susan responded, "but there's something that the world is missing with half the marriages ending in divorce. How many of those families once sat and talked about keeping divorce away from their marriage just like you and I are doing tonight? Yet something got into that marriage. Everyone involved started taking as truth things that are not true and eventually one more family was on the way to being destroyed by divorce."

It was not often that Doug and Susan had conversations

like this any longer. When they were dating and first married, they could talk for hours about almost nothing. But as the years passed, each developed their own interests and the mold seemed to be set for a marriage. Even though the topic was heavy and hit as close to them as their next-door neighbors, Doug and Susan enjoyed sharing their heart with one another.

Living in a hotel, Sam had no place to entertain his children for a weekend, so the few times he had seen them were just for an evening. Susan was always the one to drive the children a few blocks to McDonald's at 26th and Federal to meet their dad. She would return in a few hours to take the children home.

Each time they met, Susan could see a devastated man in Sam. He reminded her of the big black olive tree in the Tomlinson yard that was dying from the inside out. The tree still looked healthy, but she had been shown how the tree trunk was getting soft because of rotting inside. That is exactly the way she envisioned Sam Sullivan every time she saw him.

On one occasion when they were passing children at McDonald's, Sam ventured a question to their neighbor. "How is Becky doing?" he asked in a faltering voice, unsure if the question was even appropriate.

Susan replied, "She is doing pretty well considering the circumstances. Sam, Doug and I are more concerned about you. How are you doing?"

It was at that time that Sam shared about being terminated at the bank. He had continued to support his family from the severance package money just as he had done previously. After he did so, Sam regretted it, knowing that Becky would soon hear he was unemployed. He did not want to worry the wife he loved so very much, neither did he want to make it appear that he was attempting to get out of his financial responsibilities to his family.

A couple of visits later, Sam sent his children on to the car and then asked his neighbor Susan a really pointed question. "Have you seen any other man coming or going from the house?"

Susan replied in the tone of a schoolteacher correcting a child who was out of line. "The answer is an emphatic no! You are the only man Becky wants to see coming or going from that house, but your question is unfair. A couple visits ago Becky asked if you had another woman in the car when you picked up the kids from me. I answered her the same way I am answering you. Doug and I will not take sides with whatever is going on with you guys, and we will not be message bearers."

Susan continued, "This divorce is one of the dumbest things I've ever heard about. You need your wife and children; they need you desperately; and here we are out playing cat and mouse at McDonald's, avoiding you from seeing the woman you married."

"But the restraining order says...."

"I don't give a flip about a restraining order. You are an intelligent man. Yes, certainly you obey that order, but you have worked with legal matters all of your life. I don't know the answer, but I know there must be one! You don't just destroy a family because two people had an argument. If you and your wife both want to put the brakes on this mess, there must be a way to do it."

Sam thanked Susan and jumped in the car with his kids,

wearing his happy face, but thinking about Susan's scolding. "You don't just destroy a family because two people had an argument."

One morning while the kids were at school, Susan suggested to Becky that they go to the huge bookstore on Federal Highway to see what they could find that might help Becky through her impending divorce. Although Susan never said so, her motives were also selfish. She recognized that her own empty nest marriage was far from perfect. She feared some day being in the shape that she saw Becky living in each day and wanted to see what she could do to make her marriage stronger.

The two women spent hours browsing through book after book. The interest of most writers was on recovery after divorce. Next to nothing was found on stopping divorce. Susan did buy a couple of books for her and Doug on strengthening their marriage. She located a book specifically for empty nesters.

Despite their morning and early afternoon of bookstore browsing, neither lady discovered what they really were in search of - a book designed to get a fractured family back together.

Driving home, Susan raised two issues. "There are two things I do not understand. First, how can the destruction of divorce attack a good family and then after that happens, where is there any hope?"

Sadly, these two women had no idea what book they really needed. Even though they did not know it, the Bible addresses not only why families get attacked, but what a spouse should do about it when attacked and thousands of other helps for daily life.

There is a word that was used often in the church only a few years ago. Today it is seldom uttered. That word is *seeker*. It describes the person who has the Holy Spirit moving in their life. Without even knowing so, they are seeking Christ. In our story, we see two seekers.

We have an absent husband who has actually gone to church seeking help. Now we also have his wife and her best friend searching bookstores for the answer. If someone could only show them that families are destroyed when satan, the enemy of our souls, attacks our families. If someone could only show them that God heals hurting marriages. There is a way out and His name is Jesus.

Chapter 10

‘I’ve Had Enough”

Sam had started the process to become a licensed “Recovery Agent” in the state of Florida. That is the legal terminology for a repo guy. About 20 years ago, when Sam was studying so hard to become a banker, never did he imagine that one day he would be excited about his upcoming licensing in about a year, allowing him to legally “steal cars.”

His family situation had mellowed just a bit. Although a much longer restraining order was in place, he had run into his wife a few times strictly by accident. Most of these were things like sightings across a parking lot, but each time she responded with a wave and a smile. Sam continued to support his family just as he had the first week he was gone. Nevertheless, there was an upcoming court date over finances. Neither Sam nor Becky saw the need for it, but it was one of many things her attorney basically demanded.

“He can stop paying you and you have no recourse,” the attorney had told her. Who knows Sam the best? An attorney of a few months who had never talked to Sam in person or the woman who was his best friend, who shared his secrets, who had been married to him for a decade and a half?

Becky had been shocked many times by the terminology that had been placed in legal papers she had received. Words being used to describe Sam did not even come close to what he was. The accusation of the deep-voiced attorney sitting across from her was just too much.

“Sam would never abandon his family,” Becky objected.

"Matrimonial strife changes people in ways you would not believe," the attorney justified. "We'll prepare for the worst and fight for the best and everything will come out fine for you."

Becky thought, "What about Sam? Does anyone even care how he will come out? I cannot imagine the guy going from a banker's office to stalking around at nighttime looking for cars of deadbeats. This is one of the times in a man's life when he needs a wife the most, and I am not there for him."

"What would happen if I just said forget all of this?" Becky blurted out to the attorney.

"The court would frown on that," the attorney replied with a stern face. "Once you have instituted proceedings you need to carry them through. This is the stage in divorce proceedings when many people get cold feet, just as you are. It's completely natural and to be expected. A year from today you'll be thanking me that I did not let you back out. There is a better life, one free of abuse, waiting for you with someone else."

A chill ran down Becky's spine at the very thought of someone taking Sam's place in her life. She could not understand why she could not halt everything. After all, she was the one who instituted the divorce. Her patience was wearing thin.

"I've had enough!" Becky shouted as she banged her hand on the armrest of the big chair as she stood. "Lies, that's all this thing is built on, your lies. I tell you a glass was accidentally knocked over during dinner and somehow you make it to be Sam sent it crashing it to the floor in anger. I tell you he spanked one of our kids with his hand when they deserved it, and you make it look like he beat the kid to a pulp. I tell you that he is a good man who is meeting his obligations to his family, and you still want to make him look like a crook. I've had enough!" Becky ended with the same three words that had begun her monologue of anger.

The attorney rose from behind his desk and went to where Becky was standing. With an air of compassion, he placed his hand on her shoulder and consoled, "I've been at this a long time and know how difficult it can be. I've been through three divorces myself. We're all set for today so why don't you go home and calm down. Take care of yourself and plan to do something you enjoy. You have an entire life sitting in front of you."

As Becky got into the elevator, she was there alone and began to think. "I'm taking counsel from a man who has failed at marriage three times? The man can't tell fact from fiction in his court papers, and I am allowing him to write the future for our entire family? I've had enough." Becky repeated that three word phrase for the third time in three minutes.

Just as her attorney had suggested, Becky went home. Just as he had suggested, Becky was going to plan to do something she enjoyed. She enjoyed being a wife and a mother in an intact family; one with everyone happy with themselves and with others in the family. One way or another, Becky was going to see that happen.

Imagine with me if someone delivered the car or truck of your dreams to you today. They knocked on your door and handed you the keys and the title to the most beautiful vehicle you had ever seen. No strings attached, it was yours free and clear. Wouldn't you be disappointed to discover that your vehicle, as beautiful as it looked, had no engine? It was powerless. Not only would that be a great disappointment, you could not go anywhere in that car.

You could sit in your new car all day long but it would not take you anywhere. There was no power. It would still be a car, but without an engine. That would not do you too much good, would it?

Where Becky was right then could be compared to your car without an engine. She wanted so desperately to see her husband come home and this nightmare ended. Becky's husband had even sought out a church where he had an unfortunate experience. Becky had looked through aisle after aisle of books seeking help. Both Becky and Sam had their "new cars." Now if someone would only show them the source of power, our Lord God, this could be one more marriage on the way to restoration His way. That is the only way that brings true happiness and lasting results to a once fractured family.

Chapter 11

Not Exactly a Dinner Party

While Sam waited for his paperwork to come back from the state to get him on the road to licensing as a repo guy, he worked with Jerry most nights. In addition to keeping his time occupied, Sam was learning the business from an expert.

One night while they were out together in the tow truck, Jerry said, "Anita and I want you to come to dinner this evening if you don't have other plans."

Sam replied with a chuckle, "Me? Have other plans at this stage in my life? I will have to let my social secretary get back to you on that." Both men laughed and Sam agreed to come.

That night at 6 P.M. Sam arrived at the small Lauderhill apartment that Jerry and Anita shared without benefit of a marriage license. Sam knocked on the door and was surprised by the cleaned up version of Jerry that greeted him. For the first time since he met him, he did not have dirt under his fingernails and his shirt was clean.

"Come in, come in. Anita, this is that character Sam that you hear so much about. Sam, this is my wife…er... girl... Well, anyway this is Anita." Sam thought Anita must not get introduced very often, considering the way Jerry danced around what to call her.

Sam suddenly became aware of a fourth person in the room. It was a woman who looked about Sam's age. She was an attractive and neatly dressed blonde. She attempted to smile, but Sam knew enough about people to recognize the air of nervousness and uncertainty that she carried.

"Sandy, meet Sam, the man of your dreams. Sam, this is Sandy. I know you guys are perfect for each other. Your names even seem right together, both starting with S and all."

Sam uttered a "nice to meet you" and offered Sandy a smile, but inside he was trembling. Jerry had said nothing about a fourth person coming to dinner, much less a person who he thought was a good match. How Sam wished he was back in his hotel room, alone, instead of standing awkwardly as part of this foursome.

"I work with Sandy at Broward General," Anita volunteered. "Sandy and I share our troubles with each other. When Jerry started talking about you, I just knew Sandy had to meet you. You guys are so much alike."

All of a sudden Sam did not want to be back in his hotel room. He wanted to be in his own home with Becky and their children. How could it be in only weeks he had gone from the comfortable lifestyle with his family to being introduced to a woman that he was expected to date, to marry, to move in with or something? Sam had never felt more out of place in his entire life.

In the next few seconds, Sam developed his game plan. He would be polite but quiet, eat dinner, and then excuse himself just as quickly as possible without being rude.

Jerry crushed those plans in his next sentence. In one breath he revealed everything that Sam did not want this woman to know-and then some.

"Before his divorce, Sam was a big wheel at a bank downtown. He had a marriage that just didn't work out, kind of like yours, Sandy. He's living in a hotel temporarily. Wait until you see his wheels. You guys are going to really hit it off."

Anita jumped into the conversation, almost as if planned, to tell about Sandy.

"Sandy is an R.N. at the hospital and she has her own apartment. Her husband used to be a musician and a bag boy at Publix. He left Sandy in the middle of the night for a woman in Cincinnati."

"Not only that," Jerry added, "He used to be married to the woman he left Sandy for. I guess he didn't learn his lesson the first time around."

This was one of those sentences of Jerry's that, to Sam, was like fingernails scraping across a blackboard. Sam was wishing very much he could be back with his own wife and family, and here Jerry was making jokes about it.

"How does pizza sound to everyone?" Anita asked. "I think I have a coupon. What do you guys like on your pizza?"

In the social circle Sam had been in until recently, a dinner invitation had an entirely different meaning. He and Becky had dined with friends and business associates at the finest yacht clubs and country clubs Fort Lauderdale had to offer. Many times they had enjoyed meals in the homes of prominent local physicians, politicians, and pastors. They had returned meals with these people in their own home, always with a carefully planned menu and elegant table setting.

It was not the way that Sam had been raised, but he and Becky had climbed the social ladder, due to his banking position. Not since college had he been invited to dinner and then asked what he liked on his pizza.

As an aside, I wonder why none of those prominent pastors the Sullivans had dined with ever took a few minutes to talk about Jesus. I also wonder if any of Sam's social friends or business associates had been Christians. If someone had only taken time to share the Gospel with him, Sam would be so much better prepared to face all that he had gone through recently. Even more important, our friend Sam would also be prepared to one day stand before his Creator, as we will each be required to do.

Sam's indigestion that night was not from pizza. It was from his situation. Jerry and Anita used every opening to attempt to play matchmaker. They had an agenda tuned finer than a candidate's political debate. Regardless of what Sam would say, either the host or hostess would spin it in an attempt to hook up Sam and Sandy.

Sam was terrified at the thought of ever being close to any woman other than Becky. He had been faithful during their entire marriage and did not intend to change at this stage, regardless of the circumstances. Sandy seemed very nice. In fact, under different circumstances and if he were not already married, Sam could very easily be attracted to her, especially if he didn't have two other people trying at every opportunity to match them up.

After a couple of hours, Sam was able to thank Jerry and Anita for dinner and find an excuse to leave. He said goodbye to Sandy and told her how much he had enjoyed meeting her, thinking that would be the last time their paths would ever cross.

The following night Sam was shocked to receive a phone

call from Sandy. He was furious that Jerry had given her the number of the company's cell phone that Sam carried.

Sam was surprised at how easy it was to talk to Sandy. They really did have a lot in common and he could see how they might be friends someday. The following night Sam called Sandy and they talked even longer. On this night Sam confessed that he was not divorced, but had a divorce pending in the courts. Sam and Sandy agreed to meet the following evening "just for coffee."

Sam laid down his cell phone feeling like a teenager who had just landed his first date. The love for Becky that he had hung onto so strongly all these months was suddenly interrupted. As the evil one likes to do, Sam had allowed satan to confuse love and lust in his mind. That first "just for coffee as friends" was quickly followed by more phone chats and a movie date.

The details can be omitted, but it will suffice to say that Sam moved out of his hotel room shortly. All of a sudden his impending divorce from Becky seemed not to matter. The new place where he was living was so far away from 26th and Federal that Sam could not arrange to see his children often.

It would seem, by man's standards, that another marriage was on the way to its death. But wait, God has not worked yet!

Chapter 12

"My Brother"

"Sam, this is Becky, your wife. I know I'm not supposed to talk to you, but there's something I have to say. I don't care if they put me in jail or something for calling you, but I still have to do it."

You could have knocked Sam over with a feather. Becky was the last person in the world he expected to hear from, and he didn't quite know how to handle the call, especially since Sandy was staring at him and wondering who was on the cell phone. Mostly Becky talked and Sam listened.

"I am so sorry about everything that has happened in these past months. Sam, I have made some horrible mistakes, and I need to ask you to forgive me."

"That's no problem," was about all that Sam could get out.

"Honey, I won't blame you if you say no, but Sam, we need you at home. I do not know how we will work out all of this legal mess that I've created, but I'm asking you to please come home and let's start all over again. Don't answer me now, but please think about it," Becky concluded.

It was almost as if Becky knew there was someone else in the room with Sam, and she did not want to embarrass him any more than she had already.

"Yeah...I'll, uh, get back to you on that." Sam stumbled through the words, unsure how to end the call. "Thanks for calling me, though."

After Sam hung up, the two people involved with that call had thoughts that were 180 degrees different from each other.

Becky was devastated. She had gone way out on a limb and it had snapped underneath her. Through the years she had heard Sam on enough evening banking phone calls to know that his "I'll get back to you on that," meant no way, absolutely no way. Becky hated herself at that moment for what she thought she had done to her family. She did not know that God had other plans.

Sandy had been staring at Sam during the short phone call. "Who was that, honey?" she cooed as he put down the cell phone.

"Ah.... it was just, ah... about my kids," Sam reported.

At that moment, after hearing the deceptive phone call, followed by Sam's deceptive explanation, Sandy knew this relationship would end just like her last one when Tom, her short-term husband, left her a note and went home to his covenant wife in Cincinnati.

Not wanting to either create a fight or to end the relationship right then, Sandy said nothing. Nevertheless she knew that it had been Sam's wife on the phone. She also knew that at some point Sam would be going back to her.

As it happens so often in our problems and in our crises, God is moving and we never know it.

The following night Jerry and Sam were doing a repo from a large apartment complex down the road in Pompano Beach. The complex had a reputation as a singles' place.

Just like always, Jerry turned off the lights and they cruised through the parking aisles looking for the car they were to pick up. Up ahead was a car that matched the description to a T.

"Naw, that couldn't be it, because it looks so good. That car is spotless," Jerry said as he got out of the truck to check the VIN number.

"It matches," Jerry said as he came back to the tow truck. "There is something weird here about that car. It's just been waxed and it has tire dressing. There's not a mark on it. On top of everything else, there's a note on the windshield asking the tow truck driver if I could knock on the door of apartment 111. Normally I would ignore it, but this one has my curiosity up. Sam, you're the people person, so maybe it would be good training for you to go knock on 111 while I hook up. It's right in front of us so I'll have your backside, but just don't go inside."

Suddenly the repo business was not quite as attractive to Sam. He could handle having people chase him back into the tow truck cab, but going to someone's door in the middle of the night, he thought was beyond the call of duty. Nevertheless he did not want to appear chicken to his boss, Jerry, so he started for the door.

Sam reached the door and knocked about as lightly as he could, hoping members inside would not hear him. He was shocked and took a step backward when the door suddenly flung open.

"Hello, brother, thanks for coming to the door. I wasn't sure you would," the man wearing a bathrobe said.

Sam thought his life had come to an end. The man was

so happy and his car was being repossessed. Sam was certain the man was going to shoot him or attack him.

"I just wanted to give you both sets of keys. Here's the registration. I don't know if they will need it, but I thought it might help," the bathrobed man announced in a voice that was just too happy for the middle of the night, especially when a tow truck is hooking up to your car. Sam did not know what to say. All he could do was motion for Jerry who had his hands on the lift control raising up the car.

Jerry thought something was wrong and ran to the door. Just then Sam noticed the music coming from inside the apartment; not the kind of music he listened to, but some kind of music that was just, as Sam described later, "totally peaceful."

"Hey, brother, my name is Russ," the man said as he extended his hand to shake with both Jerry and Sam. "I'm the owner of the car, or at least I was trying to be the owner of the car. I'm sorry to get you guys out. Please tell the bank I waxed it today, and it's been serviced regularly. There's nothing wrong with her that I can tell. It will make somebody else a great car."

"Wait a minute. You know we're here to repo your car not to buy it, right?" Jerry said, never one to beat around the bush.

"My brother, I sure do," Russ replied. "It wasn't supposed to happen this way, but something got crossed up at the bank. I have been talking to them almost daily about a voluntary repossession, even asking where I could bring the car. Yesterday morning when I called, the collector refused to talk to me and said someone would be out to get the car tonight.

"I may not have the money to make my car payments, but since I don't have a job, I have plenty of time and elbow grease to make her shine, and maybe help the bank recover more money. It embarrasses the heck out of me to have this happen, but between losing my wife and my job, there's nothing I can do."

Russ had just said more than Sam wanted to hear. Even though they were in the same boat, this character had an absolute glow about him.

"I know what it is!" Sam thought. "He's on drugs. That's where all his money goes. He buys drugs instead of paying his bills. No wonder he's so happy."

"A Christian is to be a person of their word," Russ volunteered. "I promised that bank I would pay for the car, and I will, even if I don't have it. It may take a while but they will not lose a penny on me."

Sam thought what a dream customer this character would be for any bank. Jerry just looked confused and didn't know what to think. He could have handled it better if the guy had stood outside yelling at him while the car was hooked up. Jerry almost felt guilty about taking away a car from someone who was so cordial.

It was almost as if this Russ could read Jerry's mind. Looking directly at Jerry, Russ said, "Don't feel bad about taking my car. God has a plan and a purpose in all of this. Several of my brothers at church arc praying for my marriage, a new job and my car. They are claiming by faith that I can catch up on the payments and get the car back before it's sold."

The two repo guys did not know how to respond. Neither

one had ever seen someone act quite like this guy. One of them mumbled some polite goodbye, and they headed back to the tow truck. They pulled away, with the repo in tow, watching the former owner standing in the doorway wearing a bathrobe and waving goodbye to them.

"Woo hoo! Takes all kinds," Jerry laughed.

Jerry might've been laughing at this Russ guy, but something about him had gotten to Sam. He said very little for the rest of the night.

"How could a guy just like me, no job, no wife and now no car be so happy?" Sam asked himself. "Christian? Is this what being a Christian really means? I always thought being a Christian was like the pastors at the country club, about like everyone else, but just a little more polished. A few weeks ago I got a new view of Christians when I tried to visit the church, but no one knew I was there. Now this guy comes along...."

Jerry's jesting about not enough money in the collection plate to make the car payment and Russ probably being a mental case really bothered Sam. He had just encountered a real Christian, one who was an example for others to follow, and he liked what he saw. How Sam wished he had been alone so he could've asked Russ some questions, to ask him how he did it.

Early the next morning riding along in the tow truck, disrupting one family after another by repossessing their vehicle, Sam realized he needed a real job. This was not for him. Sam also realized something else in those late hours. He wanted to know more about being a Christian. Were they all like Russ or were they all like the other "Christians" he had met through his life?

"My life is a mess and my family is in a mess. How I wish I knew someone who could explain to me what it really means to be a Christian and to have the peace that character had," Sam pondered as they drove along with Jerry jabbering as usual.

We could say Sam was now a sincere seeker. Praise the Lord. Now who will be there to lead him to the Lord?

Chapter 13

Full Disclosure

One Saturday morning a few weeks later, Jerry called Sam. "Hey, want to go hunting with me the Lauderdale way and have some fun? I've got a repo that's like shooting fish in a barrel. This one is going to be great."

Half an hour later, Jerry picked Sam up in front of Sandy's apartment building. "You are going to love this one, Buddy," Jerry's voice rang with excitement. Once again Sam wished he was not sitting in a tow truck. Sam thought how that same truck could be used by Jerry to tow disabled cars to repair shops, to start cars with dead batteries or to change flat tires. Nevertheless, Jerry in his small black tow truck, dressed in his grungy black clothes, seemed to delight in disrupting people's lives. Sam did not really want to hear what Jerry had in store for this Saturday.

"One of my regulars called me today, a banker from Hollywood. He was reading the morning obituaries and saw where a man died whose car they need to repo. They have been chasing him for weeks. His funeral is at 11 A.M. at a church in Hollywood and they suspect his family will be driving the car there. This will be a first, yanking a car out of a funeral line up."

Sam wondered if this guy could be for real. Did he have a heart at all? He probably got his start repossessing his mother's car or something.

As only Jerry could do, he jabbered all the way down I-95 to Hollywood Boulevard. During that trip, Sam regretted ever starting the process to become a repo man, a recovery agent, in the state of Florida.

Many times Sam had looked at his tailored suits, now hanging in Sandy's closet and wondered how he had gotten to where he was. What he would give to have a reason to put on one of those suits, check his appearance and head to the bank. How much more he wished that Becky would be the one to joke, "You look sharp today, handsome. Better look out for all those young tellers."

Becky was comfortable enough in her marriage that she could make quips about her handsome husband without any fear there would ever be a problem. Marital fidelity was something that Sam and Becky had discussed in great detail. Their marriage could have been a role model for other couples striving to avoid unfaithfulness.

In his banking days, Sam would risk missing out on a lucrative loan before he would go to lunch alone with a female customer. Yes, it was all business and something accepted by the world, but Sam could not risk having someone see him with another woman and assume what was not true. As Sam climbed the corporate ladder at the bank, his office changed many times. One thing that never changed was the fact that Sam would never have a woman in his office, for any reason, with the door totally closed. Even when he advanced to the upper floors with private offices that were floor to ceiling glass, the door would always remain ajar if there was a female visitor inside.

When Becky would have an appliance repairman coming to their home and the children were gone, she would arrange for Mrs. Tomlinson to come over as soon as the service truck appeared. Neither Sam nor Becky would have a member of the opposite sex in their car without others being present.

Right after their marriage, Sam and Becky made a pledge to each other. Any time there was a situation where either of them had been tempted or following times when their own guidelines had been broken, they would tell the other spouse about it before bedtime. For example, one morning a fellow banker agreed to pick Sam up at the car dealer. Unknown to Sam, the other banker sent his secretary to bring Sam to work. That night Becky was told. You might say it was full disclosure, just like those loans Sam used to make.

Eccentric you say? Out of step with the times? Not at all. Although the Sullivans did not know the Lord, they did know the harm that could come to a marriage. They also knew the appearance of something being wrong even when every thing was above board. During the years, the Sullivans had friends whose marriages had become victims of nothing more than rumors and they were determined never to have a situation that looked like anything less than 100% marital faithfulness.

"Must be this place," Jerry joked. "The hearse gives it away."

Sam asked himself, "Doesn't this guy ever quit? Even if we spot the car we're looking for, no one would be heartless enough to pull it from a funeral." He was about to be proven wrong.

"That's it!" Jerry literally squealed with excitement. "The gray van right behind the hearse, the one with the funeral flag on the roof."

"You're really going to do it, aren't you?" Sam asked in a disgusted tone. "You're going to pull a car out of a funeral procession while the family is inside the church. Man, where is your heart?"

Jerry gave Sam a surprised look. "My heart? It is right here next to my wallet." Jerry launched into one of his laughing fits that always drove Sam crazy.

"I'm going to park out in the lot and take a walk down the sidewalk so I can check the VIN number, but I believe I can see it from here," Jerry squealed, followed by more of the disgusting laughter.

He was back to the tow truck with Sam waiting inside quicker than he could have possibly walked around the corner and checked a VIN number.

Sam wondered if Jerry always smiled like that every time he located a car. Usually they were together late at night or in the early morning hours and it was really too dark inside the tow truck, which had its dome light removed so as not to give them away.

The more Jerry laughed and smiled and enjoyed this invasion into a family's tragedy, the more disgusted Sam became. Sam's future in banking was nonexistent due to the financial crunch. Sam had been meeting his own needs and providing for his family from his savings. This repo thing was more for fun than for income. One repo in the daylight with Jerry was going to be enough to end his career as a recovery agent before it was really off the ground.

"Here's what we're going to do, Buddy." Sam hated being called, 'Buddy,' by a man who would do what Jerry was preparing to do. "I've got to grab it sideways, so you block the street for a second. As soon as I'm in place, I want you to take that blue-and-white funeral flag thing off the roof and hang onto it for a minute. As soon as the car's out of the space, plant that flag right in the middle of where the car had been." Sam was determined this would be the last time he would ever hear that sick laughter.

Jerry backed up. Sam did as instructed and grabbed the flag from the roof of the car. As soon as the car was moved, Sam put the flag down in the space and scampered for the security of the tow truck cab. Just as they pulled away a man who must have been the funeral director ran out of the front door of the church, waving his arms at them feverishly.

Jerry waved back and said, "You have a nice day also."

Jerry jabber filled the truck cab all the way back to the impound yard. Sam wasn't really listening, though. He was thinking about how far he had fallen, from that bank office to legally stealing a car from a grieving family; from the faithful love of his covenant wife, to the foolish lust of the woman he was living with.

There was something else about being a repo man that Sam could not take. Going through a divorce, Sam had read a lot about divorce. He read that a woman's standard of living drops an average of 40% after her husband leaves home. More than once Sam had seen Jerry hook up a car belonging to a woman who was the victim of divorce. Each time, Sam had imagined his wife Becky being in that situation, and he hated it.

Sam had heard stories of family destruction, tearfully related against the background noise of tow truck chains about to remove a fractured family's only source of transportation. It was heartbreaking. How often Sam wished he had the money in his pocket to give to a sobbing, abandoned spouse.

"Something's got to give," Sam thought. "There has to be a better way than this, and I am going to find it."

Chapter 14

Two Phone Calls

When Jerry dropped Sam off at Sandy's early that Saturday afternoon, Sam did not go into the building. He stood out front staring at his automobile. That black BMW, although one of the less expensive models, had always been his pride and joy. When he was a banker, a car wash service would come to the bank once a week and clean the car inside and out. Now that same vehicle had not been washed in weeks. The two front tires had grunge from the street on them. A tree in Sandy's apartment building had dropped sap onto Sam's car, in a visitor parking place.

Like so many other men, Sam's car had always been an indication of what was happening to Sam on the inside. When he was at the bank, on top of the world, the car was well-maintained and spotless. Now that it seemed he was on the bottom of the world, the car had not received any attention at all, much like many areas of Sam's life.

Instead of going inside, Sam got into his car and went searching for a carwash, even though the South Florida skies were darkening and about to bring rain.

Sam will tell you he had the car fully detailed that afternoon because the car wash gave him a great deal due to the approaching rain. In truth, that rainy day detail of the BMW spoke volumes about Sam's self-made promise from that morning to do something about his situation.

While the car was being detailed, Sam made two phone calls. One was to the long stay hotel where he used to live. Sam had a question to ask: "Do you have any vacancies?"

The second call was to his former neighbor, Doug Tomlinson. Even though they had not spoken since Sam left home, he had a favor, a big favor, to ask of Doug. There were some items at home of Sam's that he really would like to have, especially since he was going back to the hotel.

"I certainly do not want to place you in the middle of a mess," Sam said, "but I know my wife and she will have no hesitation in giving you the things that I need. If it becomes a problem, please just let it go. My marriage and your friendship are more important to me than any personal effects."

Doug grabbed a piece of paper and jotted down the items Sam was requesting. There was nothing really unusual or that might cause a problem with Becky. Sam was asking for his laptop computer, some additional clothing items, a few specific dishes from the kitchen, any mail that Becky might not have forwarded to him yet, a few family photos Becky could share with him and the family Bible.

The Sullivans only owned one Bible. It was displayed year-round in their living room, always open to the 23rd Psalm. On the two holidays each year when the family went to church, no Bible was carried. In fact, very few people at their Easter/Christmas church carried Bibles.

Doug and Susan went next door together to give Sam's request to his wife. Neither were prepared for what that request would bring about.

Susan began, "Becky, honey, Sam called us and wanted to know if we could bring a few items to him that he would really appreciate having. He stressed that if it is a problem for you, for all of us to forget that he called."

Momentarily Becky forgot about the restraining order. Her emotions were on edge and this set her off. “If he wants to rip this house apart why doesn’t he do it himself? Did he forget where we live? Oh, I forgot we’re just his family. What does the creep want? Half our furniture?”

Becky’s rage continued, “I know he’s living with a woman. I have my ways of finding out these things. Go on, go on, tell me what the creep thinks he is entitled to.”

Doug Tomlinson sheepishly raised the list that he had been holding at his side. “It’s really not much. Just his computer, these clothing items, a couple of kitchen things and the Bible.”

“The Bible! Oh my God! He wants the Bible!” Becky began to sway so much that Susan thought her neighbor was about to pass out and placed a steadying hand on her neighbor’s shaking shoulder. Doug and Susan looked at each other, unsure why asking for an unused Bible had evoked such a dramatic response. They were about to find out.

Becky repeated her remarks from a second ago, word for word. “The Bible! Oh my God! He wants the Bible!” Don’t you see what this means? I will not stand for it!”

Subconsciously, Doug took a step back from his ranting neighbor. Not only did he not have any idea what this all meant, he was unsure of what the screaming woman was about to do next.

“The computer,” Becky screamed. “I guess ‘she’ just wants to go through all of our documents so she will know how to hurt me more. As far as the kitchen things, tell her paper plates and cups don’t cost much. The pictures? No sir! She is not going to gloat over the family that she destroyed.

And the Bible, the Bible, worst of all! When do people use Bibles? They use Bibles when someone is getting married or buried. No one is getting buried, at least until I get a hold of that no good husband I used to have. So he and his tramp must be planning to get married, probably the very day our divorce is final! That's just great! Get married with our Bible, eat off of our dishes, while they laugh at our pictures! By the way, no to the clothing also! Tell him to wear something he already has to his stupid wedding! My attorney was right all the time! This thing is going to get nasty."

Doug could handle the emotions of his own wife pretty well, but this was beyond his pay grade. He suddenly decided he needed to check on a project the two Sullivan boys were working on in the garage.

Thankfully, Connie, who still carried guilt over feeling that she had started all of this in her family, was away from the home and missed her mother's explosion. Connie had a Friday night sleep-over at the home of her best friend from school, a girl named Kayla, who lived in Coconut Creek.

Kayla was quite the baker for only being ten years old. Her mom always supervised and handled the oven, but that Saturday morning it was Kayla who suggested they make each of their mothers a cake. Two boxes of cake mix were opened and Kayla gave Connie her first baking lesson.

Kayla liked to take icing of a different color and drizzle it onto her cakes for decorations. She could also write out words in icing. It was Connie who had a suggestion for what to write on the cake.

Saturday afternoon when Kayla's father took Connie home, she walked in the door and gave her mother a small, somewhat lopsided cake. The icing words on top were not real clear. Becky asked, "Honey, what does it say?"

With a big grin, Connie announced, "It says 'Daddy loves you.'"

God made quite a creature when He created woman. While Doug was in the garage with those two boys, giving supervision to a Saturday project, Susan and Becky were soon sitting at the kitchen table, crying together, and rationally discussing how Sam's request could not be in anticipation of a wedding. Half an hour later they left the Sullivan home with every item Sam had requested, plus some more items that Becky thought he might need.

What Susan missed was Becky writing a note and tucking it into the inside pocket of one of the suit coats her husband was requesting. It was cryptic enough that no one could ever prove in court that it had been written while the restraining order was in place, but it was also one fresh enough that when Sam read it, if he should, he would know exactly what it meant.

Later that Saturday afternoon, Doug Tomlinson called Sam and arranged to meet him at McDonald's to give him the items he wanted.

"How did my wife do when I asked for these things?" Sam inquired.

"She did great. No problem at all. I think you're going to find some extra things in that box also. I heard her telling Susan about some items she thought you might need."

Sam's dark sunglasses hid eyes reddened from crying. He picked up a family photo from a vacation a couple years ago and tears began to roll down his cheeks. Doug did not know what to do.

"This is hell. Pure hell. Here I stand six blocks from my family and from our family home and somehow the judicial system is saying I can't go there and I can't even talk to them. I would like to know how some judge expects me to cram 14 years of marriage into some pictures and trinkets. Doug, I need help. I don't know where to turn. I don't know what to do, but I need help."

For the next half hour the two men leaned against a freshly waxed BMW in the parking lot at McDonald's in Coral Ridge. Neither was concerned about buttons on the back of their trousers scratching the BMW. Some things just take precedent over BMWs. To be honest, our families must take precedent over everything else apart from the God who created us.

Sam drove out of the parking lot and did something unusual. He turned North on Federal Highway and headed for McNab Road. Sam could not tell you the reason, but you and I know why 15 minutes later his car was entering the apartment complex where he had met Russ, the man who cleaned up his car before it was repossessed.

Sam would tell you he was just taking a drive or maybe he was curious if Russ had recovered his car, but for some strange reason, Sam had this feeling that he needed to go to that complex on this very afternoon.

Sam was surprised by what he saw. Not only was Russ' car back, that fool was out there waxing it again. He really had nothing to say, but Sam pulled behind the car and rolled down his darkened window.

Actually, with Russ it wasn't necessary to say anything.

Maybe Sam came here today just to catch a dose of the enthusiastic spirit that Russ had demonstrated in the middle of the night when they picked up his car. Sam could hear Russ humming or singing or making some noise as he waxed his car. He noticed the BMW stop and had a puzzled look on his face. Obviously Russ did not run with the BMW type crowd.

Suddenly a big grin covered Russ' face. "Hello, brother. I told you the Lord would get my car back and sure enough He came through for me again, praise His name."

From the enthusiastic spirit Russ demonstrated right then, the night they met on the repo must have been an off night for him. Sam had never encountered such a happy and enthusiastic man as he saw on that Saturday afternoon. "Brother, you got pretty sharp wheels. Is that yours, or did you just pick it up from someone who can't pay for it?"

For the first time ever, Sam was slightly embarrassed to be in such a nice car. "It's mine-mine and the bank's together."

Russ had stopped waxing. He wiped the sweat from his forehand with the tail of his T-shirt. He set the wax can and rag down on top of his car and walked over to Sam's open window. "What brings you back to this neighborhood, my brother?"

"Well, I..., er, to be real honest with you, I have no earthly idea. Maybe I was just curious if you got your car back, which I see you did." For the first time, Sam noticed the Bible lying on the dash of Russ' car. He also saw a front license plate that read, "PRAISE THE LORD."

Russ was grinning bigger than ever by now. It was not

that synthetic smile that the photographers tell us to put on. This guy had something inside him making him genuinely happy. Sam decided right then that whatever brought him to that parking lot on that Saturday afternoon, whatever was beaming out of Russ, that is what Sam wanted!

"So how did you get your car back?" Sam inquired.

"The Lord," is all Russ said. He was beginning to sense this man was here by divine appointment. Russ bristled at the thought that his Lord God could possibly be entrusting him to lead a lost sinner to Christ. Although Russ only replied "the Lord," you can be confident that he was saying much more to God on the inside.

"What do you mean, 'The Lord?'" Sam inquired. That redheaded man sitting in the BMW with darkened windows and wearing dark tinted sunglasses had just taken the Gospel bait.

"Do you have a few minutes?" Russ inquired. "If you do, I would like to tell you my whole story. I think you will find it interesting and maybe even a little funny."

Without uttering a word, Sam edged his BMW into a parking place next to Russ' car. For one of the few times in his life, Sam felt like a phony. He had just paid to have his BMW waxed, a car that he really could not afford any longer and here this guy was out waxing his own old jalopy. You could not have pulled Sam out of that lot with a team of horses at that point. Maybe this guy seemed a little goofy, but whatever Russ had is what Sam had been searching for so desperately most of his life.

"I'm glad you came by because it's time for me to take a break anyway," Russ said, "You mind sitting on the grass under the tree?"

Sam replied, "That's fine." Maybe that's what he said but what Sam meant was, "I will sit on crushed glass if you will share the secret of your happiness with me because I am miserable."

Sitting under that big ficus tree, Russ related a story of a wife who did not want him because he had been unfaithful. The very thought of that made Sam shudder. Russ was a computer technician whose company had folded. He told of having submitted job application upon job application, but not receiving even as much as a call back. He was living on unemployment. It was enough to pay his rent, but not his car payment.

Sam had a puzzled look on his face. "I don't get it. Your world fell apart just like mine did, but I fell apart with my world, and you are about the happiest guy I have ever come across. There's something I'm missing. That music I heard coming from your apartment the night we were here for your car, does that have anything to do with it?"

Russ was sitting on the grass across from Sam, propped up against a tree. His hands were folded behind his head and his legs were crossed at the ankles and he had that smile, that smile never went away. He began to speak more lovingly than Sam had ever heard a man speak in his life.

"I saw you eyeballing my Bible and my front license plate, so I guess you assume I am a Christian."

Sam looked puzzled as he started to talk. "So you are a Christian, that's your religion, right? Look at you right now. Unemployed, without your wife, no money obviously and yet you're the most relaxed guy I have ever seen. What do you have? I want a dose of it. How do I get it?"

The sinner that had taken the Gospel bait from Russ was about to be hooked.

Russ' countenance, although still relaxed and pleasant had turned from gleeful to serious. "May I ask you a question?"

"Sure, shoot," Sam replied.

"Suppose, just suppose, that when you left here in that shiny BMW, a semi ran the traffic light at Powerline Road and scattered BMW and you all over the intersection and you died. The Bible tells us that each of us are going to stand before God after we die. If God should say to you,'why should I let you into Heaven?', what would you say?"

"Well, I've thought about death and what comes after death, but I've never considered that specific question. I guess I would tell God how I've led a pretty good life. I've done a lot of good things for people and I've never done anything really bad... ." Suddenly Sam thought about the car taken from a funeral line only a few hours before.

"The Bible tells us that we are all sinners. Take me for example. I am 31 years old. If I sinned only three times a day since I was, oh say 15, do you know how many tens of thousands of sins or transgressions that would be? I would sure hate to stand before a judge on earth with that many transgressions against me, much less stand before God, our Creator."

"So you're saying it's hopeless for any of us to get into Heaven, right?"

“On our own merit it would be, but God made a provision. He became flesh. He became a man, but a man without sin. When Jesus was crucified on the cross, He was crucified for every sin that I will ever commit. He is my Savior. The good news is that Jesus is waiting to be your Savior also. Does this all make sense to you?”

“It does,” Sam replied with a puzzled look. “But I have done so much wrong. My sins are more than three a day, maybe 300 a day. How much sin can God forgive?”

“As much as you are willing to confess and that is to be all of it. There's no halfway deal here. You acknowledge that you are a sinner. You believe that Jesus died for your sins and you accept His free gift of life eternal. Now part of this is repenting, or turning away from sin from right now on.”

Russ could tell that Sam was on the verge of comprehending God's plan of salvation for sinful man. Silently Russ asked God to give him an illustration and did he ever.

“Those cars you repo, who owns them?” Russ asked Sam.

“Legally, the bank does if they're financed, until the loan is paid,” Sam replied.

“Take that car of mine. Well, I guess that's not a good example because you did take that car of mine. Let's say your BMW there. The bank is allowing you to drive it but they still own it until it's paid for, correct?”

“Agreed,” Sam replied.

“So when you go out with your black tow truck on behalf

of a bank, you're just taking back what is rightfully yours, correct?" Russ pressed.

"Agreed again," Sam replied for the second time.

Russ looked as serious as good-natured Russ could look as he said, "Now take me and you. Who created us? God did, right?"

"Even if I am not a churchgoing person I know that God created us."

"So let's see where we are," Russ pondered. "We know that God created us, and we know that we have sin in our lives, separating us from our Creator. One way of looking at this from your line of work might be that Jesus is the repo man. God created us and wanted me and you to pay the price of a life without sin. Just like when I couldn't make my car payments that I had promised, I lost my car. I could not live a sinless life like Jesus wanted, so He repossessed me. In other words, now He has full control of my life," Russ concluded.

Suddenly Sam had a vision of some of those nights and the repo truck, the subjects that he and Jerry had talked about, and even more beyond that.

"By the way, I am praying and standing that God will 'repo' my wife and bring her back to Him and to me. I have taken a stand for our marriage to be restored by God," Russ quickly added.

Russ removed the cap from the water bottle sitting next to him. "Say this cap represents sin." He extended his right hand. "Let's say my hand represents you. You have already said there is sin." With that, Russ dropped the cap into his extended right hand.

"When you stand before God, He sees you but He also sees your sin. Now let my left hand represent Jesus, who suffered and died on the cross to take away your sin." With that, Jerry plucked the sin/cap from his right hand and concealed it inside his left. "Now when you, the right-hand, stand before God, He sees only righteousness. Jesus has taken away your sin.

"Inviting Jesus Christ into your heart not only prepares you for life eternal, but it gives you a new Best Friend, a Comforter to walk through the problems of life with you."

Sam had a quizzical look on his face. "You mean you're happy because you're letting Jesus walk through the problems with you?" Suddenly Sam remembered that Sunday morning church service on television he saw from his hotel months ago. Russ was saying the exact same thing! This is what he had been seeking when he made that unfortunate church visit.

"This is what I have been searching for all of my adult life," Sam exclaimed with joy. "Why didn't anyone ever tell me before?" A lot of blanks in Sam's life were suddenly being filled in.

"If confessing your sin and inviting Jesus into your heart is what you want to do, I can lead you in a prayer and you can do that right now, right here under this tree.

"I hate to have to ask you, brother, but what is your name?" Russ inquired apologetically.

For the first time in his adult life Sam Sullivan, banker turned repo man, husband turned prodigal, spoke directly to his Creator. Sam prayed and then Russ prayed. Both men were tearful when they came up from their knees.

"How is my family going to find out about this? My wife and kids need to be saved also," Sam said with resolve.

"We are going to be praying that someone is there to share the Good News of Jesus with your family. I pray for my wife and for my parents every day of the week. Now both you and I will be praying for your entire family to be saved. And you know what? God answers prayer!"

The two men talked for quite a while. Sam shared his entire story with the man who had just led him to the Lord. The two men were quite different, yet they were so much the same. Now they really were brothers in Christ.

Russ also shared his story. He and his wife Lori lived in Gainesville, Florida. At the time of their marriage, Lori was a Christian and Russ was not. They were college sweethearts. After they both graduated from University of Florida, they stayed in the college town they loved. They had been married about eight years.

Lori had been pregnant once and had a miscarriage, which she attributes to the stress of Russ having had an affair with an old flame. When the affair came to light, Lori immediately filed for divorce, as everyone was telling her to do, especially the people in the law office where she worked.

At one point, after the divorce had been filed, Lori contacted Russ, seeking his forgiveness and inviting him back into the marriage. As the world measures things on the scale of sin, Russ was having a good day and actually laughed at his wife. She hung up and that is the last time they had spoken. As far as Russ knew now, the divorce was on hold, but he could not imagine why.

Russ, in search of a new start, moved to Fort Lauderdale where he had gone through a series of both IT jobs and girlfriends.

One day, a stranger from Fellowship Church struck up a casual conversation with Russ on Lauderdale Beach. The man told Russ about Jesus and his life was radically changed. A few days later he was the one walking the aisle at Fellowship Church. From that day to the present, men in his Bible study have discipled a brother who took the fast track to being an on-fire Christian.

As Russ began his walk with Christ, he realized that divorce was not an option. Lori refused his calls and any mail he attempted to send her was returned marked "unknown."

The only book Russ had that told about marriage restoration God's way was his Bible. He had no restoration teaching CDs and about all he had heard about marriages being put back together was from friends who had experienced that miracle and from teachings at his church.

As God often does, he had planted the seed of faith for the hope of restoration deep in Russ' heart. Russ had been promised by God, not by man, that if he remained faithful to his marriage vows and to his Lord, one day Lori would be back at his side.

No one knew it, but Russ had saved a seat at Fellowship Church and debated ushers over it in crowded services with full confidence that one day his Lori would be sitting in that seat, as God had promised him.

"You never told me how you got your car back," Sam interrupted.

"Like I said, it was the Lord. A man I do not even know came up to me at church and handed me an envelope. Inside was the exact amount of cash I needed to recover the car."

"You're kidding me, right?"

"God gets the glory, but things like that happen when you're a Christian. He takes care of His children," Russ explained.

What Russ did not say is that even though he got his car back, he did not have a cent to put gas in it. When he was waxing his car, he was also praying that God would send someone by to be the first person for Russ to lead to the Lord. He wanted so badly to be a soul winner, and God had answered that prayer.

Sam pulled out of the parking lot with a renewed spirit within. He felt as though a ton of problems had been lifted from him. He did have a busy evening ahead of him though. He went to Sandy's apartment and loaded up his few personal effects while she was at work. He left her a note of apology and the door key on the table and locked the door behind him, feeling that he had closed one more chapter of sin in his life.

Sam called Jerry and asked to meet with him. At that meeting, Sam turned over the cell phone, charger and keys. With a thank you for all Jerry had done for him and an apology that things had not worked out, Sam was on his way to check into the long stay hotel. The man did not even have a cell phone, but he felt more connected to life than he had in years.

Chapter 15

"This One's On Me"

Although Sam was providing for his family financially, the standard of living for Becky Sullivan and her three children had dropped drastically since their separation. She was no different than the majority of other men and women who go through this horrible crisis. While Becky did her best to keep things about the same for Grant, Connie and Ryan, much was different. This foursome seldom went to a restaurant, where once they often ate out several times a week.

"Mommy, can we go to Skyline tonight?" ten year old Connie begged. "We haven't been there for a long, long time. Please, Mommy, can we go? I know just what I will eat and I won't order expensive stuff."

Twelve-year-old Grant joined in the pleadings. "It won't take much gas to get there because it is so close. I have two dollars I earned, helping Mr. Tomlinson cut his bushes. That will help us also."

Those two sentences were enough to earn the Sullivan kids a trip to Skyline Chili at 26th Street and Federal Highway. Regardless of what budget cuts she would need to make this week, Becky knew that her kids deserved a dinner out. Young Ryan did not even need to join the conversation because his brother and sister had made their case successfully.

Skyline Chili was a Cincinnati, Ohio chain of small chili shops. Sam had gone to college at Xavier University in Cincinnati and claimed he almost lived on Skyline while he was there. After moving into their Coral Ridge home many years before, Sam was excited that one of the two Skylines in South Florida would almost be their neighbor.

It was quite a sight to see Mr. Sam Sullivan, the successful downtown banker, wearing a Skyline bib over his neatly pressed white shirt and silk tie, eating Skyline's trademark Coney dogs, with chili residue falling down the front of him. Becky would always be even more embarrassed when Sam started into his chili. Long strands of spaghetti would escape his mouth and fall onto the plastic bib where they would adhere. Becky always suspected eating at Skyline somehow brought out the college boy remaining in her now grown husband.

Becky had never developed a taste for Skyline. She felt like an outsider listening to Sam order his favorite, "Chili's four-way with bean." Once she attempted to order using the Cincinnati lingo, but ended up with a beautiful chili dog, topped with shredded cheese and onion, but without a hot dog inside. In recent years, Becky usually ordered a salad while she watched the other four members of her family devour Skyline.

Becky was never quite certain if her three children really loved Skyline as much as they appeared to or if they really enjoyed watching their daddy eating with a bib, while he regaled them with stories of his college days in Cincinnati.

This would be the family's first Skyline outing since the separation, but Becky knew she had to do it. Young Connie still carried tons of guilt over having made the 911 call that instituted this family being torn apart. And Becky had talked with her daughter extensively and explained what was happening was the fault of her parents, not her. Nevertheless, many nights after Connie had been tucked in bed by her mom,

Becky could hear the soft sobs of her daughter.

If she had passed by Grant's or Ryan's rooms and listened carefully, she would have heard much the same. Regardless of what court gave the order, a parent cannot be torn out of a child's life without a lot of trauma, without a lot of heartache. Why do our pastors, our judges, and our neighbors not comprehend that basic fact?

Speaking of neighbors, you might be wondering why the Tomlinsons, the neighbors to this fractured family, did not tell them about Jesus. After all, they faithfully took the three Sullivan children to vacation Bible school each summer. Why did they not tell Becky about the only real source of help for her problems? The Tomlinsons were well respected in the church. They had raised three children of their own. For certain, they had called on Jesus many times.

Why was Becky not being told about the Savior who wanted to be her Best Friend through this crisis? To be quite honest with you, these neighbors were what we know as Sunday Christians or closet Christians. They had come from Christian families and had received Christ as children. During the past 40 years of their marriage, neither one of them had personally led anyone to accept Christ. They tithed at their church and each of them were on several committees. They were what we could call church leaders. Even though they would rejoice when someone would pray to receive Christ at church, neither one had ever taken their pulpit into the marketplace.

Why had Doug never spoken to Sam about the Lord? It was because Doug had back trouble that even his chiropractor in Old Pompano could not correct. Doug had a yellow streak running down his back. During more than 30 years of selling insurance and now running his own agency, Doug had been rejected many times as he made insurance presentations to people. Why was he so afraid to make a Gospel presentation? It is a lie that satan tells God's children about how traumatic it would be for them to share the Gospel with some lost soul and to be rejected. How many people were in Hell right then because Doug could present insurance but not present the Gospel? How many more people would Doug meet during the rest of his life where he could change their lives, if he could only loosen the tongue on matters of Christ?

That evening Becky loaded up her three children and gladly took them to Skyline Chili for dinner.

Skyline is a unique place. It is a small restaurant with both tables and a counter with stools. The chili, spaghetti, and beans are prepared behind the scenes, but orders are put together by a cook working on a long table behind the counter. One of the highlights has to be the large grill with dozens of small hot dogs cooking at a time.

Young Ryan was just like every kid who has ever eaten at Skyline as he asked, "Mom, can we sit at the counter so we can watch Tony cook?" Tony was the family's favorite counter man. He was a people person and could usually be found talking to customers at the counter as he assembled their meals.

As much as Becky disliked sitting on those stools, this trip was for the kids so she agreed they could eat at the counter. Would you believe God had it all planned for them to eat at the counter that night? Becky ordered chili and Coney dogs that night and for some unexplained reason asked for a bib.

Even though brokenhearted, she did like so many other men and women in her situation have done, stepping in and giving 110% to her kids. Now, if Becky could only find Jesus.

"Where's the banker tonight?" Tony inquired as he portioned chili over a sleeve of hot dogs he was holding on a stainless steel rack in front of him. Although the length of time that Sam had been gone from home could now be measured in months instead of in weeks, Becky had not had that question posed to her previously. She did not know how to answer.

"... Ah, Sam's not at home right now," she finally got out.

Tony never stopped preparing chili dogs, but glanced at the children on both sides of Becky. Out of respect to the children, Tony only uttered a soft, "I'm sorry."

After they had finished eating, Tony stepped around the counter with a handful of quarters that he dispensed to the three Sullivan kids. "Here, you guys can go to the ball machine and see what colors you can get out tonight." Tony knew that three kids, with a handful of quarters and his bouncy ball machine, would be entertained for a few minutes. After they each had a few balls, they would have to do the trading back and forth. Tony had chosen a wise diversion for those kids, and they never suspected a thing.

"I did not mean to be nosy when I asked about your husband. Please forgive me," Tony apologized.

Becky replied with one of her trademark small smiles. "You did nothing wrong, Tony. That's a question that I'm going to have to learn to answer a lot more in the days ahead, it seems."

Tony sat sideways on the stool next to Becky and

inquired, "Is there anything I could do?" Some men could have asked that question and it would have seemed they were attempting to come on to Becky, but Tony was about ten years older and a hundred pounds heavier than her own husband. Becky recognized immediately that Tony was not flirting, but was sincerely concerned. The tone of his voice and even the way he held his head said "What can I do to help?"

To Becky it was an extremely non-threatening conversation. She glanced over her shoulder and saw the kids busy putting quarters into the machine and then exchanging the small colorful bouncy balls with each other. For some odd reason, she opened up to Tony like she had never done to anyone except Susan Tomlinson since this nightmare all started.

Becky told about the argument and the 911 call. She even told about vomiting on the street in front of the courthouse when she realized the impact of the restraining order. Tony's assistant scampered to keep orders filled while Tony sat and listened to Becky. One time, he handed a waitress a second handful of quarters to take to the kids at the bouncy ball machine, knowing that would keep them occupied for a few more minutes.

Many times she had heard Sam tell about Tony's compassionate heart, but Becky had no idea what kind of listener this man was. She thought later that he was probably wasting his time dishing out chili when he had such people skills, but she had no idea God had Tony exactly where He wanted him to be.

Tony did not speak. He only gave a few nods of agreement and a few "uh huh's" as he allowed this woman to talk and talk and talk. Under any other circumstances, Becky would have been uneasy having a man sitting next to her, without her husband present and having a protracted conversation. Something about this time was different. It could've been the look of concern on both of their faces, or the fact that Tony was wearing a chili stained apron that made this different. It could have been the orders flying around them, with customers and waitresses quite literally under their noses.

Becky told of Sam losing his job and of his suspected living arrangements with a nurse somewhere. She told of futile trips through the bookstore looking for help. Her eyes teared up as she finished her monologue with, "I don't know what to do. I am at the end of my rope."

Had this been any other customer telling the same story, Tony would have given them a hug, possibly even sharing a few of his chili stains with their clothing, but something was different about Becky. It was as if a shield was around her.

Tony thought for what seemed like the longest time while he stared at an imaginary spot above the front door. Finally he spoke. "We had another customer a while back, a guy named Tom. He was a salesman so everyone got to know him. He was a regular several times a week, always ordered the same thing, and then he just disappeared. We all thought something had happened to him.

"About a month after Tom's last visit to us, we received a card from him. Seems he had suddenly gone back to Cincinnati where he had come from and had remarried the wife he walked out on. Tom thought he owed all of us an apology for being a poor witness, whatever that means. The comments on that card did not sound like they had been written by the same Tom we all knew, since he was kind of rough around the edges when he was here. Nevertheless, he and his wife had gotten remarried and now they own a flower shop or something.

"I stuck the card on the bulletin board in the back since he wanted to apologize to everybody here. In it he gave a phone number and said if we had another customer in the same situation, he or his wife would be glad to talk with them. Maybe that was just for you. Want me to get that card for you? It's been here long enough that everyone has read it by now."

Becky agreed and Tony disappeared into the back of Skyline. He returned with a greeting card and again took the stool next to Becky. He opened the card and held it out in front of Becky. Tony began to read as he pointed to each word, almost as if Becky could not read it for herself.

She was thinking about her situation and only caught about every other phrase that Tony read: "Forgive me for being a poor witness"... "God restored our marriage."... "Never imagined the happiness"... "anyone else... ."

Tony handed over the card which Becky stuck into her purse. As Tony stood, he picked up the check saying, "This one is on me. You have enough on you." Becky's watery eyes turned into full-blown tears, accompanied with a few sobs.

Twelve-year-old Grant, playing the role of his mother's protector, quickly came to her side to see what was wrong. He stared intently at Tony as if Tony had caused the tears.

"No, honey," Becky told her son. "These are tears of joy. Sometimes people cry when something good happens to them."

Grant's reply was a barometer of what that child was feeling deep inside. "Nothing good ever happens to our family. Nothing good is ever going to happen again."

Becky thanked Tony profusely for both the free dinner and for the kind, listening ear. She gathered her children, headed for the car, and started home. Two quotes Becky had heard within seconds of each other rang over and over in her mind: "Nothing good is ever going to happen again" and "Never imagined the happiness."

Becky pulled into the driveway of the Sullivan home determined to first help meet the needs of her hurting children and then find out what this Tom and his wife had experienced. Sadly, Becky was soon caught up in her own needs and hurts, and that card gradually worked its way to the bottom of her purse, where it was forgotten.

Chapter 16

111 Prayers

On that Saturday afternoon when Sam had been led to Jesus Christ, Russ invited him to church the following morning. After the invitation to church was given, Sam had a flashback of his bad experience at the high steeple, frozen people church that he had attended only a couple months prior.

"Thanks for the invite," Sam responded. "But I'm not much of a church type guy. I guess I'll just grow my new faith by myself. Churches always seemed so, well you know, Russ, so distant, like there was nothing there for me."

Russ' reply could well be the measure for every man who will ever prepare a sermon again. Never losing that big grin, he said, "It may sound a little selfish, but when I leave church, I ask myself what happened, what the pastor taught that will help me make it through another week. It's really not selfish though, because the Bible tells us we can't give out what we don't have. Maybe that would be like when you were a banker and you only gave out loans, but no one made deposits. That could put a bank in worse shape than what most of them are already in today," Russ finished, widening his grin even more.

Sam was amazed at how this guy could come up with illustrations. For the second time, he thought about his church visit experience. No one was giving out that day and no one was receiving. Maybe there really are churches that are more like the one I saw on television.

"I'll make you a deal," Russ offered. "If you will attend

church with me once, I will never invite you back again unless you want to go."

Sam's heart was gladdened by what he had just heard. Russ, whose spirit he admired so much, apparently wanted to build a relationship with him. At least they would be seeing each other again or he would not have an opportunity to invite him to church for the second time.

With a lot of reserve, Sam agreed to the noon service on Sunday at Fellowship Church with Russ. He calculated that he could endure one more church experience for the sake of building a friendship with a man whose spirit, peace and enthusiasm he wanted to copy.

As Sam prepared to drive away, Russ had one request. "Brother, would you mind picking me up for church tomorrow?" He never disclosed the fact that his car did not even have enough gas in it to get to church and back. It is easy to see how Sam was so intrigued by this man. He had nothing, but yet he seemed to have everything, and that is what Sam was seeking.

Even though Sam had dissolved a sinful relationship, moved back into the hotel, given up a job, and basically given up his friendship with Jerry all late Saturday, that night he enjoyed the most peaceful night's rest since he had been forced from his home. On Sunday morning, as Sam was preparing to clean up for church, he grabbed the remote control and turned on the televised church service that he had seen by accident months before. This time, he listened as he showered and shaved.

Looking in the mirror, Sam realized that he was smiling. It was the same type of smile that he had seen on Russ. Sam silently wondered if he was catching whatever it was that

Russ had. Deep within, he hoped so.

Sam was not vain, but that morning he stood there, razor in hand, and stared at his image in the mirror. Who was the guy looking back at him? Was this a banker or a repo man? Was this a faithful husband who loved his wife dearly, or was this a prodigal spouse? Was this guy really as happy as he looked in the mirror, or was he just faking the peace he wanted so badly?

The process of discipling Sam into a mature Christian had been taking place for less than 24 hours. Nevertheless, Sam remembered something that Russ had told him under that tree yesterday afternoon about calling on Jesus. Sam laid down his razor on the edge of the sink, closed his eyes and prayed.

"Jesus, please show me this day who I am. Thank You for the peace I feel this morning. Please take care of Becky and our kids while I am away, Amen."

Our friend, Sam Sullivan, now a Christian for less than 24 hours, did not realize he had started something that would become a habit for the rest of his life. As Sam grew in the Christian faith, he would have several prayer opportunities every day. Nevertheless, for all those years, every morning when Sam was alone in the bathroom, he would stand before his mirror and talk to God.

Sam walked over to his closet at the hotel to select something to wear. Most of his clothing was wrinkled from Saturday's move. Russ had told him that people dressed in many ways at Fellowship Church, some dressed up and some dressed down. Sam did not want to over dress and stand out. He pulled a pair of gray slacks and a blue shirt from the rack. In a moment he found a tie that matched.

On the way to the lobby that Sunday morning, Sam grabbed his traditional cup of coffee. As he walked to his car, the BMW was literally shining from Saturday's wax job. Sam thought how much different he felt than the last time he headed to the car on the way to a church.

After picking up Russ, the two men headed for Fellowship Church. Sam was expecting a church about the size of the one he'd visited with 85 people. Was he ever in for a surprise! Cars were lined up to get onto the church property. Men in orange safety vests were directing traffic. Each one also wore a Russ type smile. Time and again Sam witnessed vehicles stopping to allow someone else in front of them. Even though this was Fort Lauderdale, it was so unlike the dog eat dog, every man for himself rush-hour traffic that Sam had endured in downtown Fort Lauderdale for years.

In a couple of minutes Sam was in a parking place and he and Russ were exiting the vehicle. The driver of the car parking next to them went out of his way to say good morning to the two men and to shake their hands.

Outside the door to this church, just as at the other one, Sam also encountered men standing around. Only here they were shaking hands and greeting people. Their sincerity amazed Sam. It was not as if someone had said, "You are assigned to the east door to greet people and you must be friendly." Before Russ had escorted Sam to a seat, five or six people had shaken hands with him and said good morning. Sam sensed that he could have said to any one of them, "I have a big problem. May I tell you about it?" and they would have taken him aside and prayerfully heard the concern.

When the two men were sitting down, Russ asked Sam to leave the seat vacant between them. Sam, whose emotions ran on the edge these days, thought that something about him must be offensive. That is, until Russ leaned over and said with a bigger grin than ever, “I save a seat every week for my wife. You never know.” As he finished he gave Sam a little wink.

“Odd,” Sam thought. “His wife is in North Florida, and he is saving a seat for her in a church in Lauderdale. Now that is some kind of faith.” Sam thought about this for a second and then looked to his right. He saw that the seat was unoccupied. He thought about a scripture verse, from possibly Luke, that Russ had shared yesterday, saying that all things are possible with God. Sam managed to open his bulletin over the seat and to get his elbow in front of it to indicate the seat was saved. For just a second he could envision his wife Becky sitting there.

Sam thought it was almost as if Fellowship Church was growing hundreds of little Russ'. Sam had the name wrong but the concept right. This church was growing people, not in the mold of an individual, but in the mold of Jesus.

Everyone came in carrying Bibles, it seemed. Sam was thankful that he now had his family Bible in the hotel room, as it was too cumbersome for anyone other than the Jolly Green Giant to carry to church. It wasn't long before an usher with a stack of Bibles came down the aisle where Russ and Sam were sitting. A Bible was offered to anyone who did not have one. For a moment, Sam forgot his banking days were over, as he thought about how some of the concepts utilized for making people feel welcomed, important and comfortable by this church could be used to make bank customers feel welcome.

As the service started, a praise band was playing. Sam leaned over to Russ and whispered, “That's the same kind of music I heard playing in your apartment that night we picked up your car, isn't it?"

"Sure is. It's called praise music. I keep *Stop Divorce Radio* on my computer 24/7. It really helps."

Sam determined right then he needed to find *Stop Divorce Radio* on his laptop to also have praise music playing in his hotel room around the clock.

So far, this church was very different than the first church he visited. Sam really sensed that he was a part of all that was happening at Fellowship Church. They introduced people by name. He heard how to make a prayer request and determined that he was going to request prayer for his career and for his marriage.

The music that followed was unlike anything Sam had ever experienced. Everyone sang the words from large overhead screens. Beyond that, they sang like the words were from their hearts. Sam liked everything about this place called Fellowship Church.

When the pastor came out to preach, Sam felt the hairs on his arm bristle. "That's the same guy," he halfway laid across the empty seat and whispered to Russ, in a voice too loud to really be called a whisper. "That's the guy I saw on television. That's the guy that looked right at me and talked to me Sunday morning when I was so despondent. That's the guy that got under my skin and sent me out looking for a church. I listened to him this morning, but I never dreamed he was right here in town."

It really did not matter that Sam's whisper could be heard by about six other people around them. Each of them just rejoiced that the television ministry from their church had touched another soul for Christ.

After the sermon, when that pastor "drew the net" and invited people to come to the front for prayer, Sam Sullivan, dignified, reserved banker, was one of the first out of his seat. Right afterward, in a private prayer room, another brother from the church was the cleanup batter on the hit for Christ that Russ had fielded so well the day before.

Sam walked out of that church with a new Bible in one hand and a couple of praise music CDs in the other. But even greater, Sam had found an inner strength that would carry him through the problems of today, tomorrow, and for the rest of his life. Praise God.

Russ was more than thrilled that the man he led to Christ the afternoon before had responded to a public invitation. As they got into the car, Russ wished so badly he could spend time with Sam that Sunday afternoon after church and talk to him about the decision he had just made for Jesus. Since Russ was totally broke, he could hardly invite Sam out to a late lunch on Sunday. Russ was thrilled with Sam's invitation as they drove out of the church lot.

"Would you allow me to take you out to lunch to thank you for helping to get me on the right path?"

When Sam's car pulled up to Longhorn Steakhouse, he was embarrassed that Russ was bringing his marked up Bible inside. Later, the two men could be found sitting in a corner booth inside Longhorn. One was introducing the other to just a few of the thousands of promises contained in God's Holy Word.

"Fellowship Church is not all perfect," Russ conceded. "We are people just like you. Every one of us has problems.

Today there were people there at church from bankers to bums."

Did you ever say something and before the words had even landed you regretted saying them? That was Russ right then. How he regretted using the two phrases banker and bum in the same sentence, for Sam had gone from being a banker to almost being a bum. Even though he might be driving a fancy car, it was a lot of show. The man was unemployed and on the way to a divorce, and Russ had just referred to bankers and bums.

"My brother, I am so sorry, I did not mean to say what I just did. I pray you understand I was not talking about you." For the first time Sam saw Russ without a smile on his face, as he humbly apologized for his mis-speak.

Sam touched Russ' arm across the table as he spoke. Russ was clearly upset by what he had just said to a one-day-old Christian. "Don't worry about it," Sam said. "I didn't even notice until you said something about it."

Suddenly Russ' beaming smile returned. "You know what else I think? I sense in my spirit that before long you're going to be a banker again. Beyond that, I sense in my spirit that you and Becky are on the way to restoration, so you keep saving a seat for her at church every week. My brother, after God restores your job, please see if your bank needs an IT guy. Our field is so bad they do not even give out cardboard boxes, just ship you out to the wolves. I do not know how people make it who do not have the Lord and His Word to depend upon."

Sam had only promised Russ that he would attend church with him once, but from his comments it sounded as though Russ was expecting him to be there every week. In the days ahead, not only would Sam be there every Sunday morning, but also every Wednesday night, as well as for many of the special events.

"The marriage restoration? Yes, I pray that happens and soon, but as far as being a banker again, I can't see that. The way the economy is, banks are dropping people so fast they're running out of cardboard boxes, but maybe once I get some other things in my life straightened out God has another door he's going to open for me." Sam was quite certain that door was not going to lead back into the repo business.

Those two men having a meal together was so much different than the way Sam and Jerry used to be together. One relationship was hopeless and the other was filled with hope beyond hope.

In the days ahead, Sam began to get a burden for Jerry. He was even praying that Jerry and Anita could somehow find their way to Fellowship Church to share what he had discovered.

That Sunday afternoon in the prayer room at church, Sam had heard about being baptized in obedience to the Lord's command. Fellowship Church had their baptisms at the beach in Pompano right at the foot of Atlantic Boulevard, late on a Sunday afternoon. They used the service to be a witness to people on the beach. Having a couple hundred people present to watch 20 or 25 being baptized did attract attention. It also attracted questions, some of which, when answered, led to people accepting Christ as their Savior.

Russ had been baptized a couple months before, and now Sam could hardly wait for the next baptism service when he could make his public statement of faith for Christ.

The two men became the best of friends in the days ahead. They sat in church together, always with empty seats on either side, ready for their wives. Once all the walls were down, and it became obvious how broke both men were, they had meals together but not at Longhorn. They dined at places like McDonald's on 29-cent hamburger night.

Each time the two men were together, they would always pray that God would "repo" their wives and restore both of their marriages.

Somewhere along the way, after a few weeks, they decided they both could save money if Sam moved into the empty bedroom in Russ' two bedroom apartment and helped with expenses. Sam wanted so much to be like his mentor. What better way to get to know him better than to share an apartment with him?

During the day, both men were busy seeking employment. They filled out applications online and even had a few job interviews, but neither had the first job offer. You can be assured apartment 111 became a house of prayer. Those two guys prayed for employment so they could support their families. They prayed for their families. Many other needs and people were the recipient of apartment 111 prayers. Our ever faithful Lord God was hearing and honoring their petitions.

Chapter 17

Three Roses

On the Saturday that Sam had the Tomlinsons ask his wife for a few other items from home, including the family Bible, Susan had calmed Becky down.

When that couple left the home, Becky appeared to be normal, or at least as normal as possible for this nightmare time in her life.

Like so many people going through marriage problems, Becky's foremost concern was for her children. If the children were happy, it seemed, she was happy. This day was an exception. Connie had gone to a birthday party for a friend, and the two boys worked in the garage all day building their own version of a race car. Becky was left alone with her thoughts. There was nowhere she had to be until she dropped the kids off at school at 7:50 A.M. Monday.

Unfortunately, Becky did not know the Lord. She had not discovered what so many people going through the same crisis have discovered; that God heals hurting marriages. Becky could have spent this quiet weekend reading her Bible, in prayer and fellowship with her Lord. Instead, she allowed her imagination to take control.

From the time the Tomlinsons left for home with the items Sam requested until Monday morning, Becky saw no other adult. Instead, she listened to the lies satan was telling her. Every piece of information the children had ever innocently repeated to her, she combined into one great falsehood. She knew that another woman had become involved recently. She knew of Sam's new career. Ryan, like any innocent seven-year-old had told his mommy about what daddy was saying on the cell phone to other people.

Instead of allowing the Holy Spirit to speak hope to her, Becky had allowed satan to speak lies to her. She was certain their marriage was doomed for divorce without any possibility of reconciliation.

Monday morning when she dropped the kids off at Middle Drive Elementary, Jack Stinson, Ryan's second grade teacher, had sidewalk duty. Their other two children had also had Mr. Stinson in the second grade, so he knew this family.

As the kids were getting out of the car, Mr. Stinson walked over to greet Becky and to say good morning to the kids. If Becky had been wearing sunglasses, a lot of heartache may have been avoided. Jack Stinson noticed Becky's eyes. They were totally bloodshot from over 24 hours of crying. He knew from Ryan that his father was not living at home. Not only had Ryan volunteered that bit of information, his classroom behavior had begun to demonstrate that fact.

Jack asked, "Becky, are you all right? You don't look so good."

"We're just having a rough time at home right now. Sam moved out."

"I could tell from Ryan's behavior in the classroom that something was going on in his little life. Not having daddy at home would certainly do that to a seven-year-old. I guess I need to talk to you about Ryan's behavior. Could I call you tonight?"

"Yes, that would be great. Thanks for offering," Becky

replied. Even though the anticipated phone call was from a teacher and dealing with her son's behavior, Becky looked forward all day to that phone call. Up until then, the only men she had related her problems to had been Tony at Skyline Chili and Doug Tomlinson, their next-door neighbor, but always in the presence of his wife.

That evening the anticipated telephone call did not come. Becky said goodnight to all three kids and tucked them in bed. She turned on the television and sat there staring at the screen, but not watching. Not only had her husband rejected her, her emotions were so raw that she took the failure of a male teacher to call her to be rejection.

That night at 10:30 P.M. the phone rang, and it was the teacher, Jack Stinson. He had such compassion in his voice for what the family was going through with Sam having left. Jack described what Ryan was doing in the classroom to be disruptive and gave her a couple of suggestions to help her youngest son.

Mr. Stinson just ventured onto the edge of talking about the Sullivan family's personal problems. Jack promised to keep Becky updated on how her son was doing. She hung up the phone and was thrilled that a man was showing interest not in her, but in her feelings. He really wanted to help.

The following evening when Becky heard the phone ring at 10:30 P.M. she knew it had to be the teacher. Jack gave Becky a report on the good day that Ryan had at school.

The red flags in Becky's head should have started waving when she was asked, "What kind of day did you have, Becky?" Instead, she was just thrilled that she had an understanding man to talk with. That evening the phone call lasted for over an hour, much longer than was needed to say,

"Your son had a great day at school."

During that call she discovered that Jack Stinson could relate to what she was going through so well because he also was in the process of divorce from an unfaithful wife. Becky shared more that night than she should ever have told any other man.

The next morning at 7:50 A.M. when Becky dropped the kids off at school, for some reason Jack was on sidewalk duty again. The cheerful good morning greeting he gave Becky far exceeded what was said to any other parent dropping off a child. Becky felt like someone was watching and was most reserved as she returned Jack's good morning greeting.

Someone was watching. It was her Lord God, wanting Becky not to find a new man at the school, but to find the new man in Sam that He had created just for her.

That night at 10:30 P.M. there came another school report on Ryan. This time the call lasted until after midnight. Becky hung up, experiencing the thrill that the evil one puts into an individual when he attempts to arrange things like those that were happening to her.

There was a call from the teacher every night all that week. By Friday, having spent hours on the phone together, she felt she knew Jack pretty well, and hurt for what he was going through just as he did for her. Jack invited Becky to meet him for coffee on Saturday night and she quickly accepted. After all, he was her son's teacher and they were both concerned about what he was going through as his parents divorced.

Susan Tomlinson was asked to watch the kids while Becky went to "a meeting" she had to attend. Becky had justified it to be so innocent, yet she had to cover up where she was going.

Susan sensed something was not right when Becky left the house. She was dressed up and had on more makeup than she had worn in months. Not only that, Becky was bubbly and happy.

As soon as Becky was out of the house, Susan called her husband next door and said. "Something's going on. It's one of those things one woman can sense about another woman."

Jack had asked Becky if they could meet for coffee at a Starbucks in Tamarac. Becky assumed Jack must be living in that area. In fact, he did not want to be seen out in the evening with the parent of a student, so he had dragged Becky all the way across town, where hopefully no one would recognize him.

Becky would have done well to remember an old adage from some very wise counselor: "Men give affection to get sex, while women give sex to get affection." Nevertheless, Becky felt like a queen sitting in a coffee shop, having a man pay attention to her. She ignored the red flags that were waving in her spirit.

For the next week, the nightly phone calls continued. Soon little Ryan and his behavior were not even mentioned in the nightly calls. It was all about Becky and Jack.

That weekend they planned to go to a movie together, once again far away in North Lauderdale. Obviously the Sullivan children could not witness their teacher picking up their mother for a date, so the couple arranged to meet at McDonald's, where she would leave her car.

When Becky talked to Susan Tomlinson about babysitting for her to attend another "meeting," Susan knew she had to have a woman-to-woman talk with Becky. Susan cautioned about what she might be getting involved in, but Becky was defensive, as could be expected.

"Susan, if you do not want to watch the kids, just say so, but don't try to read something bad into my having a meeting to attempt to make our family better," Becky defended. In truth, the only way her "meeting" would benefit her family would be if she married Jack, which had crossed her mind more than once in the past couple weeks. She seemed to be forgetting that neither she nor Jack were divorced yet. She was also totally overlooking God's plan of one man for one woman for a lifetime.

On the night of her "meeting" (also known as a date), Becky was intentionally subdued when Susan came over from next door to babysit. Nevertheless, her attractive appearance gave away the kind of meeting that Becky must be attending. Susan had given her speech previously, so all she could do was pray for God's protection around Becky, wherever she was going.

About an hour later, Doug Tomlinson walked next door to check on his wife and the Sullivan gang. He often did this because those kids reminded him so much of his own when they were that age.

As happened so often, Grant, Connie and little Ryan persuaded Mr. Tomlinson to take them to McDonald's for ice cream. As they pulled off of Federal Highway and into the McDonald's lot, Ryan spoke first.

"Look! "he exclaimed, "there's Mommy's car! Her meeting must be at McDonald's!"

Doug Tomlinson's inner sense, already suspecting that something was amiss, now kicked into high gear.

"Hey kids, how about if we get ice cream at the drive-through? We can take it home and eat with Mrs. Tomlinson. You know what kind she would want."

"No, no" Ryan squealed. "We want to go inside and see mommy." Young Connie joined in the pleas to go inside so they could see their mother. Grant, at age 12, was wise beyond his years and said nothing, suspecting something was not right with his mom's car being parked only blocks from their home.

The three kids were relentless in their desire to go inside. Even an alternative visit to the fancy ice cream place down the street was refused. Doug Tomlinson had no choice except to allow the three kids to go into McDonald's, not knowing what might be found.

As soon as they hit the door, all three kids went in different directions in search of her, but their mother could not be found. When they ordered, 12-year-old Grant decided he was not hungry for ice cream, nor for anything else. Grant had woken up late a couple of nights and had heard Becky and Jack's phone conversations. His youthful imagination ran wild that night at McDonald's.

A great lesson for every person going through marriage difficulties is to remember that children are smarter than we give them credit for. They may not even do well in school, but they have a way of flushing out deception in the home, often at a great emotional price to themselves. This is what had happened to Grant that night.

Doug Tomlinson sat at a table with the three kids. Grant

was sullen, not eating, and said nothing. The usual joy found on the faces of Connie and Ryan was just not there. Doug wondered if the two younger children suspected something as much as their older brother and as much as he did. He wondered where Becky could be at that very moment. Being the eternal optimist, Doug wondered if she could be sneaking out to meet with Sam, which was prohibited by the restraining order. That is the only thought that he could carry from that abandoned car being there.

Once back at the Sullivan home, Doug took his wife Susan aside and told her what he had found. They agreed to put the kids in bed that night and to stay there together to talk with Becky when she came home and to find out what was going on.

Across town, Jack and Becky had gone to a movie. Becky was surprised when Jack reached for her hand in the darkness of the theater. She was surprised and shocked, but yet flattered at the same time. Sitting there holding hands, Sam was far removed from Becky's thoughts. It felt so good just to have some attention from a man.

After the movie, walking out of the theater, Jack had his hand on the small of Becky's back, as if to say, "She's with me." They went to a nearby IHOP for dessert. Jack got his leg against Becky's under the table a couple times. Suddenly Becky must have taken notice of the red flags waving in her spirit. She pulled her legs back and away from Jack's.

After they left IHOP, once again Jack opened the car door for her. He went around to get in the driver's seat. He sat in the car and made small talk with Becky. She wondered why he had not started the car. Details of the next five minutes can be omitted. It is sufficient to say that a wrestling match ensued in the front seat, and Becky was the winner. She won only after threatening to call the school board.

Neither spoke on the 15-mile drive back to the east side of Fort Lauderdale.

Becky was trembling deep inside. Jack pulled into McDonald's, behind Becky's car and made only one comment, "Monday I'm going to ask to have Ryan moved to another class." The compassion she had sensed in Jack's voice previously was gone. There was not a word of apology for what had happened.

It seemed that every time Becky drove her car these days she was crying, and this late-night was no exception. She felt like such a fool, thinking Jack really cared about her but all he was after was...

After pulling into the Sullivan driveway, Becky, aware that she would see Susan inside, made an effort to get herself put back together. She dried her eyes with the back of her hands and headed for the front door. Becky was shocked to find both Doug and Susan Tomlinson sitting in the living room waiting for her.

Becky's appearance had been immaculate when she left for her "meeting." She returned with reddened eyes, messed up hair, and a blouse hanging halfway out of her skirt. It was obvious that she had experienced a problem.

Doug related the McDonald's incident with the kids and finished by saying, "Becky, I do not know what is going on, but I caution you that you are going the wrong direction for you, for your children, and for Sam. Susan and I are behind you 100%, but we cannot be put in the middle of things like tonight. Could we help you? We've known you and Sam long enough that you can be honest with us."

The tears flowed as Becky emptied her soul to the Tomlinsons. At one point, Doug sensed this needed to be a woman-to-woman talk, so he excused himself and went out the kitchen door, heading for home through the gap in the fence that had been used for so many years by both families.

About an hour later Becky found herself alone, feeling very foolish, feeling very used, and hurting deeply. What was the answer? She and Sam were getting divorced and she thought she had met the perfect man, even though they were meeting by deception. She sensed that once the divorces were finalized, their relationship could come out into the open and things would be different for them.

Even though that was her envisioned future, Becky needed relief now. Where was she to find her help? She knew she was not the first woman to go through a divorce. In fact she was not the first on their block to be divorced, and the others all seemed to be making it. What was the answer?

That night when Becky had first walked in the door of her home, she was so surprised to see both of the Tomlinsons sitting there and she was so upset, that she tossed her keys on the sofa. After everything had settled, she went to put them into her purse. Somehow the wrestling match in the car had totally turned everything upside down in her purse. She opened it to find the greeting card that Tony had given her at Skyline.

Becky read the words written on that card again and again. Something about them really got under her skin. Is it really possible for a marriage to be restored like this guy in Cincinnati had claimed happened to him and his wife? She suspected her marriage to Sam was too far gone for that now. In addition, her attorney had warned her about the danger of any false hope of reconciliation.

Becky held that card in her hand for the longest time. She wondered what was worse; false hope of reconciliation or a wrestling match with her son's teacher in the front seat of a car, defending what belonged to Sam. She wondered how that card made its way back to the top of her cluttered purse. She wondered how she ended up on the fast track to divorce. In summary, Becky wondered.

Finally, she could take it no more. Even though it was well after midnight, she picked up the phone and dialed the number that was on the card. A woman's voice answered on voice mail and seemed so full of life, so happy, so joyful. Surely this woman had not really been where Becky was tonight.

Becky did leave a message after the tone, but she seemed to get some of the facts confused.

"Hello, my husband has another woman and he has filed for divorce. He's never coming back. I don't know what to do. Can you help me?"

Even though her facts were all wrong, Becky felt something inside her that seemed so right for making that call.

By the way, Becky was not the only one who had the facts mixed up. Several months later it was disclosed that Jack Stinson was a married man. This came out after another female parent had made a complaint for a situation similar to what Becky had endured that night. Jack is no longer a teacher. Becky was so thankful that when she confessed everything to the Tomlinsons that night, she had not disclosed the man's name.

The Monday morning after Becky's experience and after her phone call, a woman in Cincinnati listened to a voice mail message from South Florida and said aloud, "Thank You, Jesus, for one more marriage on the road to restoration."

That woman named Betty returned Becky's call that afternoon. It was surprising how much her problems had been like what Becky was experiencing. Yes, her husband Tom had been touched by God and had started home in the middle of the night, driving straight through to Cincinnati.

Betty said their marriage was now better than ever. They owned and operated a flower shop and enjoyed working together. Betty talked about how she had a marriage restored by God.

Becky was surprised to learn there was a large marriage restoration ministry in Pompano Beach, just a few miles north of her. She had called that afternoon and they had mailed an introductory package of restoration material to her.

Betty and Becky also talked a lot about Connie, the Sullivan's 10-year-old daughter who had made the 911 call that seemed to set all this in motion. The little girl still carried a lot of guilt over the call and despite Becky's best efforts, Connie blamed herself for her daddy being gone.

Betty had some great suggestions for helping young Connie redevelop her self-esteem. It was quite a telephone call, and it ended with Betty praying the most beautiful prayer for the Sullivan's marriage that Becky had ever heard.

Late that day, a florist delivery truck pulled up in front of the Sullivan home. When Becky answered the front door, she was asked to sign for two deliveries. Becky was shocked. She had no idea who would be sending her flowers, much less two orders. Becky went back inside carrying a beautiful floral table piece and a smaller order wrapped in the green florist's paper.

Becky opened the envelope attached to the table piece. Inside was a card that read, "God heals hurting marriages." Underneath was written Luke 1:45. Down in the corner of the card in small script was the initial "B." Suddenly, Becky remembered that Betty had said she and her husband owned a flower shop in Cincinnati.

I tell you, the tears flowed that afternoon as Becky realized that someone cared about her and about her marriage.

The green florist paper had a note on the outside to please place unopened on Connie's pillow.

That afternoon, after Becky picked the kids up at school, young Connie could not wait to get home to open the surprise that her mother told her was waiting on her bed.

Running into the house and to her room, Connie tore off the paper to discover three red roses with a card that said, "Jesus loves you." Becky told her daughter that she had talked to a woman that day who owned a flower shop. That lady cared so much about the Sullivan family that she had sent the flowers.

I wish you could have seen Connie searching for the place and a vase that was just right for her roses. A week later, after those roses had long been dead, Connie would not allow her mom to throw them out. Mother and daughter made quite a project out of pressing those three roses.

Only God will ever know how three roses totally turned around a little girl's wounded spirit. From that day forward, Connie was alive again and her mom's best friend.

If God can send flowers to a home that brighten it up so much, could He not send a husband and daddy home ? Yes, He can and will if only people are praying.

Chapter 18

"Is This Seat Taken?"

On the Sunday morning following Becky's disastrous results from going to a movie with an opposite sex friend, she was feeling low. She was concerned what rumors Jack might spread at the elementary school about her that could filter back to her children.

In truth, Becky realized her mistake and put the brakes on what could have been a major stumbling block in the restoration of her marriage. Apart from having accepted the date, her behavior was above reproach.

She and the children were all up early with nothing special to do that day. Grant, the Sullivan's 12-year-old son was fast approaching adolescence. He counted the days until he would be an actual teenager. Grant wanted to be part of anything that would make him a teen instead of a child.

Becky was sitting at the kitchen table drinking coffee when Grant came to her with a request.

"Mom, can we go to Fellowship Church today? I heard at school about a neat youth group they have. Could we go please just this one week? If you take me I promise to be good all week. If my dad was home I know that he would take me if I asked."

Grant had just said the magic words that could win him just about anything he needed: "If my dad was home." Even though it was neither Christmas nor Easter, after her experience the evening before, Becky felt a need to go to church. She checked online and discovered that Fellowship

Church had a 12 noon service. She thought that would break up the day for her family.

At 11:45 A.M. Becky's car joined the throng of others heading in and out of Fellowship Church. Grant sat tall in the front seat, excited that he was about to do something with the teens. Becky sensed something different about this church from their Christmas/Easter church.

This would be the first time in her life that she took the children to church without a husband. Her fears were quickly alleviated as an attentive church volunteer spotted the fractured Sullivan family as first-time visitors. The two younger kids were escorted to their Sunday school rooms where they discovered they both had friends that went to Fellowship also.

Grant was literally strutting as he went upstairs on his own to the youth group that he would later describe as "really cool."

Becky was a shy, reserved person. She was terrified as she walked to the sanctuary door of a church with 5,000 seats. Another female greeter made her feel welcome almost instantly and escorted her to a seat near the back, as Becky had requested. There was something about this church that she just liked right from the beginning.

The auditorium filled quickly as service time approached. A few latecomers had difficulty finding seats. About 15 rows straight ahead of her sat a tall, lanky man. The seat next to him was unoccupied. Time and again someone would stop and attempt to get into the seat. Becky thought how disappointed that man must be that the person he was saving the seat for never arrived. No one sat there for the entire service.

Becky could not see it due to the big guy in front of her, but one seat over from the tall, lanky seat saver was a much shorter red-haired man who was also a seat saver. The person he was saving a seat for did arrive, only Becky did not know that seat was for her. She had no idea that out of all of the services on a Sunday at the church and out of all those 5,000 seats, God had arranged for her to sit about 25 feet from her husband, without either of them even knowing the other was there.

Becky was surprised how comfortable she felt in that service. Unlike their Christmas/Easter church, many people at Fellowship Church sang along. She enjoyed the music and she could relate to the pastor's sermon. The events of the previous night were all placed at the foot of the cross. Becky discovered on that Sunday morning what had been missing for so many years. She just knew this was the answer. No, she did not consider Fellowship Church the answer, but on that morning she was introduced to Jesus Christ, Who is the answer for each of us, for every valley of life we ever encounter and for every mountain we must climb.

At the end of the service, the pastor extended a gospel invitation for people to openly acknowledge Jesus Christ as their Lord and Savior. He invited people to the front of church for prayer and to take a stand for Christ. Shy little Becky was so moved that she was one of the first people out of her seat and headed up the aisle toward the front.

Russ, sitting by his saved seat had never seen Becky in person, but he saw her picture often as it sat alongside his wife's photo on the guys' kitchen table, where they prayed each evening.

"If either of us ever sees the other one's wife, we'll sure recognize them," one of the two men had told the other some evening when they were praying for their wives.

As Becky passed by Russ' seat, that man jumped as if he had been shocked. He was so totally unprepared that he did not know what to do. In the vision that he and Sam had, their repentant wives would arrive at church, take a seat next to their husbands, and probably hold hands through the entire service. Nowhere in the vision did they imagine one of their spouses sitting through a service without knowing they were there.

Russ reached across the empty seat and literally grabbed Sam's arm, at the same time pointing with his other hand toward the woman who was quickly making her way to the front. Sam's immediate response was to want to follow her to the front. Russ did not let him out of the row.

"God can handle this without your help," Russ whispered to Sam. "You have done your part in prayer, now this part is God's." Neither man even remembered the restraining order. That was one of those moments when what was happening in the spiritual seemed to exceed man's law.

Sam stared at his wife standing with bowed head before the pastor. Sam wept without even attempting to wipe away his tears. Over and over Russ was saying, "Praise God." Each one seemed to get louder than the previous. The people around those two men knew something was happening, but no one could have suspected what it was.

Sam almost begged Russ to let him out of the pew so that he could join his wife. When Becky left the front with a female counselor to go to a private prayer room, Sam saw his wife's face for the first time outside of a courtroom in many months.

When the service was dismissed, Sam turned to Russ and asked, "What do we do now?"

"Church is over so we go home."

"But what about Becky? Should I go find her?"

"No sir," Russ replied. "You and I are going to be praying like we've never prayed before, but you cannot get in God's way right now. He will deal with your wife without your help. He asked you to be faithful in praying and you were. The rest is up to God. Do you remember how many times we have agreed that it is more important that our wives be saved than our marriages to be healed? The Lord can save your wife without your help. The marriage restoration will come, but this moment is for God and Becky."

Those two men sat in the car in the parking lot and prayed and prayed and prayed. Sam knew that if Becky were there, his children must be there also. They prayed that the kids would be touched just as Becky had been.

When Sam finally started his car, he attempted to drive through the parking lot, looking for his wife's car. Once again, Russ had to remind him that God was working right then and did not need Sam's help.

Sam insisted they pass up their usual Sunday afternoon fast food lunch. He wanted to go straight home and be there should Becky call him to talk.

That afternoon Russ caught Sam packing some of his belongings. Russ had been the victim of a couple of false starts toward restoration and he knew that was part of the process. He chose his words very carefully not wanting to destroy Sam's hope, yet at the same time not to have him expecting what might not happen on this day, nor any day in the near future.

Russ knew the restoration of the marriage of Sam and Becky would take place, but according to God's timetable and not Sam's.

"My brother," Russ began, looking just about as serious as Sam had ever seen him look, "God has given us a miracle today. It looks like Becky gave her heart to the Lord. That's what we are praying for, above all else. Now that miracle number one has happened, miracle number two, that of marriage restoration will come, but you need to let it come in God's time and not at the time you want."

With a questioning look on his face Sam asked, "But why did God have her sitting so close to us if He did not want me with her today?"

"God gave you a glimpse, just a glimpse, of what He can do. Out of the six weekend services at Fellowship Church and with about 5,000 people in each, that's 30,000 people, Becky sat near us, probably without even knowing it."

Russ was 100% correct. Becky had seen the tall guy saving the seat next to him, but she had not seen the small redheaded guy next to him. When she walked that aisle, Becky had no idea that her husband Sam was even in that building.

"I suspect," Sam began, "that Becky will be calling me this afternoon to tell me what happened to her this morning, that she gave her heart to the Lord. She will be inviting me back home if not this afternoon at the least Monday sometime. I'm just getting a few of my things packed."

Russ wisely replied, "Have you ever seen the pendulum on a clock? It could be going along tick-tock-tick-tock in a pretty small range, but if you pull that pendulum all the way to either side and let it go, it would fly to the other side. That is exactly what happens when a marriage is being restored. If you will, Becky has had her pendulum pulled all the way over by God today. Now satan is going to try to take his licks. My brother, please do not set yourself up for a disappointment. God is at work, but it's God's business and not ours."

Sam agreed with his roommate and Christian brother, but nevertheless he just knew that Becky would be calling. The restraining order would be dropped and he would be home again. He was sure the process was going to start on that Sunday.

The telephone in apartment 111 did not ring all Sunday afternoon and evening. Sam continued his job search Monday morning down in spirit because Becky had not called.

Like all of us tend to do, Sam had forgotten the big miracle that God had given him, the miracle that he was praying for, but which he really expected to happen deep in his heart. God allowed Sam to see that his wife was becoming a Christian. Marriage restoration may certainly be coming, but just not as Sam wanted it to be on that Sunday.

Meanwhile, back at Fellowship Church, Becky had repented of her sin and had invited Christ into her life. She had the most wonderful middle-aged female counselor in the prayer room. After hearing about Becky's pending divorce, Kim, the counselor, also prayed that Becky's marriage would be healed and restored.

"If you can be reconciled with the Lord, you sure can be reconciled with your husband," Kim had counseled.

Leaving the prayer room, Becky and Kim found 12-year-old Grant with a youth pastor in the huge lobby of the church. Much like his mother had done, the youth pastor explained that Grant had prayed to receive Christ that morning.

Mother and son embraced and cried. They were now also brother and sister in the Lord. Anything that had ever been an obstacle between the two was now knocked down through the shed Blood of Jesus.

After picking up Connie and Ryan from Sunday school, Becky discovered that although they did not understand at all yet, the gospel message had been presented to each of their classes on their level.

The Sullivan car was a place of joy as Becky pulled out of the church. Becky agreed they could stop for lunch on the way home. She pulled into a fast food place not far from the church. In fact, it was the same place where her husband and Russ would have been sitting, eating, with their Bibles opened, had not Sam insisted on hurrying back to the apartment to be there if Becky should call.

Do you realize that if Sam had not wanted to take things into his own hands, that within an hour of his wife receiving Christ as her Savior she would have walked into a restaurant and found him sitting there before an opened Bible? The rest of the story could have gone an entirely different way, if only Sam had not thought that God needed some help in restoring the Sullivan marriage.

As soon as they were home, Becky got the kids inside and went running for the Tomlinsons to tell them what happened to her that day. As you can imagine, they were thrilled, but at the same time they both were embarrassed that they had lived next to Sam and Becky for so many years and had never come straight out and talked to either of them about their relationship to Jesus Christ.

"I'm still confused about something though," Becky said. "My prayer counselor talked about my marriage being restored. Tony at Skyline Chili talked about my marriage being restored. Now that I am a follower of Christ, would anything really be different at home if Sam were here? I don't think so. We would still fight over everything. I just don't know what to do. Besides, the divorce is probably too far along to be stopped at this stage, or at least that's what my attorney implies."

Becky suddenly stopped talking and remembered her conversation with the woman in Cincinnati. She could not remember the woman's name, but she vividly recalled a statement by that woman whose husband had once been a prodigal right there in Fort Lauderdale. He had even eaten at Skyline just down the street from them and had gone home to his wife. She had thought many times about that woman's words.

"You should consider that wedding band to be fused to your finger. It was placed there on your wedding day, with God as your witness. No person, no circumstances, nothing, should ever cause it to be removed. But even if you do physically take your wedding band off, God has placed another band, a covenant, around the hearts of you and your husband and that one will never be removed."

"Oh, Susan, what does God want me to do? Is there any way out of this mess?" Becky wailed as she embraced Susan. Doug was standing beside her and praying like he had never before prayed for any marriage, including the Sullivan marriage.

"If I could just be by myself for a while to figure it all out," Becky said.

Susan came back with a reply that was uncharacteristic for her. "Yes, maybe you need to be by yourself, but not for you to figure it out. If you need to be by yourself it is to hear from God what He wants you to do."

Doug Tomlinson suddenly had an idea. "Becky, you know that cottage we have on the lake in Valdosta, Georgia? Some weekend why don't you let the kids hang out with us, you know we would love that, and you drive to Valdosta and spend a weekend in that cottage. You know it's not very fancy, but is it ever quiet. I think that's just what you need. We even have a door key hidden up there. We won't be going for several months, so you pick the weekend and the place is yours. It only takes six or seven hours to get there and if nothing else, the change of scenery would be good for you."

Becky suddenly recalled the material that she had received from the marriage restoration ministry in Pompano. The packet had arrived on a bad day and she had stuck it in a drawer unopened. She wanted so badly to get home and see what was inside that large envelope.

Does God really have an answer for her family? I know that He does, just like for so many other families, if we would only look to Him.

Chapter 19

"Raised to Walk in Newness of Life"

On a Sunday afternoon a few weeks later, Sam and Russ started east from the apartment on Atlantic Boulevard in Pompano Beach as far as they could go. The calm waters of the Atlantic Ocean lay just beyond the parking lot and public beach. This was the day of Sam's baptism and he was excited. Sam found a parking place and the two guys, wearing shorts and T-shirts, joined the crowd already on the beach.

Russ had introduced Sam to wearing T-shirts that proclaimed his faith. He often felt like a walking billboard for Christ when he would be in a store and catch someone reading the words of faith that his shirt proclaimed. Even though Russ was living on next to nothing, he had purchased a new-faith-declaring shirt and had given it to Sam as a gift to wear for his baptism.

The first time that shirt would have water on it would be when one of the pastors from Fellowship Church gently lowered Sam backward under the waters proclaiming, "Buried with Christ in baptism... ." Sam understood both from Russ and from the baptism class he had taken at church one Sunday that baptism did not wash away sins.

"They dip cows in Texas and it doesn't even kill all the ticks. So baptism can't be expected to take away our sins," Sam had heard in his class.

Sam checked in as a baptismal candidate. How he wished that his wife Becky could be standing beside him, awaiting baptism with him. That would be symbolic of her having given her life to Christ, just as Sam had done. He just knew that if both he and Becky knew Christ in a personal way, their marriage could be a success. If nothing else, he prayed that his wife could be here to at least witness his baptism.

Sam was not attempting to use trickery to get his wife back, nor was his new found faith being lived out in hopes of impressing Becky, so that she somehow work through the legal jungle so that he could hear an invitation from her to return home. Sam Sullivan was living his life 100% in obedience to the call of Christ. In short, Sam was the real thing now.

The assembled crowd sang a song and comments on the significance of baptism were made by the pastor he had seen on television, the senior pastor at Fellowship Church. After that, four people at a time were helped into the waters of the ocean and several pastors waited there to baptize them. Sam was in the third group to be baptized that day. When he was directed into the water Sam could not believe that he was greeted by the senior pastor, who would be baptizing him.

Do you recall that despondent day one Sunday months before when Sam sat on the edge of his hotel bed defeated by all that had happened to him? He had turned on the television to watch the Sunday news programs and the station was broadcasting a church service. Sam was certain that the pastor was staring directly at him as he called people to Christ. Now that same man was smiling at Sam and preparing to baptize him.

If there were ever a mountaintop experience in Sam's life, this was it. On that Sunday, watching television, Sam never imagined he would even see that pastor, much less be honored to hear him preach every week. Now this man of

God was about to baptize Sam Sullivan.

You have to understand this was not a celebrity issue with Sam, because he had once been among the ranks of the movers and shakers of Broward County. Sam could have called scores of the wealthy and the famous by phone and be put right through to them. His thrill over who was going to baptize him into the Christian faith was not one of being immersed by the senior pastor, as some might have. Sam's thrill was because he had seen God moving in every step of his life. As Sam stepped up to that pastor he was thinking, "If God can arrange all of this, putting our family back together to serve Him is no big deal."

Sam Sullivan had no idea what all God was putting back together for this new servant of His.

"Buried with Christ in baptism. . ." was the last thing Sam heard as he was gently lowered backward into the water, symbolic of the old man, the sinful man, being buried.

"...and raised to walk in newness of life," was heard a second later as Sam was lifted out of the water.

In his excitement, Sam forgot to close his eyes as he was being lowered into the water. As he was brought up, the salty ocean water stung his eyes and blurred his vision. He could only follow the shadows of others exiting the water.

Just as he was handed a towel, he heard a voice that he recognized, but could not place the person.

"Sam, my brother, I am so proud of you today. The disadvantage of going to a big church is that you miss people at other services. I never knew you were attending Fellowship Church."

Sam raised the towel to his saltwater burned, bloodshot eyes, hoping to be able to see who was addressing him. As his vision cleared, Sam discovered that the person addressing him was Mr. Dunnigan!

The man's name was really Jonathan Dunnigan or John Dunnigan as he was known by his family and close friends, but to Sam this man had never been anything other than Mr. Dunnigan. He was the president of the bank where Sam had been employed.

Mr. Dunnigan was so far above Sam on the bank's chain of command that Sam had never spoken with him, except in a few meetings. Everyone knew that "Dunnigan" was the make it or break it guy at that huge bank. The bank's president and founder spent his time with civic and promotional activities, but it was Mr. Dunnigan who ran the bank.

The old Sam would have at least thought, "You fired me and now you have the nerve to talk to me?" Instead, the first thought of this new redeemed Sam was, "Praise the Lord, we go to the same church!"

"Our closest friend was being baptized today, and I just happened to be here to witness your baptism as well," Mr. Dunnigan explained. "Now there are at least two of us in that huge building praying for the salvation of others. Actually I suspect there are more, but I do not know a single strong fellow Christian in the hierarchy of the bank, except for you."

Sam's vision had cleared enough to give him a clear look at the man addressing him. He had never seen the man except in the finest of suits. That day he wore a T-shirt of faith much like Sam's, a pair of shorts, and was barefoot. Sam did not know the man even had feet. Even now though,

Dunnigan literally reeked of class and authority. He was indeed a banker's banker.

Mr. Dunnigan chatted away as if Sam were his long lost best friend. Sam was busy thinking of the best way to tell Dunnigan that he was no longer a bank employee. A few months ago, although Sam would not have met Dunnigan at a baptismal service, if the two men had met Sam would have had no problem telling Dunnigan what he thought about him and about the bank for ruining a man's life. This time something was different.

"Sam, every time I witness a loved one or friend being baptized, I think of my own baptism," Dunnigan stated with a look of remembrance. "We all know that baptism does not take away sin, but I felt the cleanest in my life when I was being raised out of that water, 'in newness of life.' It was as if I had never sinned."

Mr. Dunnigan continued, "A few years ago I was in the hospital for a couple of days with chest pain. Any wonder why a banker would have chest pain? Instead of showering, I spent two days in that bed and bathed in a basin. After I was discharged and went home, I took the greatest shower of my life. After the hospital bracelets and needle bandages came off, I just stood under the water letting it cleanse me. I can compare how I felt with all that 'hospital' washed off my body, to how I felt about my soul on the day I was baptized."

Mr. Dunnigan continued to complement Sam on the open stand for Christ that he had taken that day by being baptized on a public beach. Most of the onlookers did so with curiosity, but there are always a couple of hecklers. Sam heard nothing that was being heckled today.

"Thank you, Mr. Dunnigan," Sam replied. "My Christian

faith is new and I have so much to learn, but how different my life is now."

"Please, just call me John when we're at church activities. The 'Mr. Dunnigan' can be for the bank, but when we're together as friends and Christian brothers, I'm just plain old John."

"Plain old John" had just knocked the props out from under Sam. The man fires him from the bank and then he expects them to be on a first name basis.

"I get it," Sam thought. "This is one of those tests of forgiveness that Russ has always told me would come." With his eyes still burning from his open-eyed saltwater baptism, Sam was determined to pass this major test of forgiveness.

"John," Sam started. Did he ever feel funny addressing Dunnigan by his first name, while the guy was wearing a pair of shorts and a T-shirt. Nevertheless, he knew what had to be done and he continued. "I want to forgive you for anything that happened at the bank. That is now all covered by the Blood of Jesus."

John Dunnigan replied, "No problem, no problem at all. I admire a man who can ask another man for forgiveness. That is going to carry you a long way in life. Well, I'll see you tomorrow at work."

Sam had no idea that "John" did not know he was not at the bank any longer. He had assumed that the president was aware of another officer being terminated.

"I haven't worked there for several months. I was terminated."

"What happened?" John Dunnigan asked with a puzzled look on his face.

"I was told that the bank was restructuring and I was no longer needed. I guess the economy just caught up with things."

"What bank are you with now?" Dunnigan asked.

Sam wondered, "What do I tell him? That I was hanging out with the guy who does repos for his bank? That up until I got saved a few weeks ago I was on the way to becoming a repo man, a recovery agent, once I got licensed? Do I tell him I cannot find another bank job? I wonder what Dunnigan knows about unemployment? I wonder if he could build on that?"

Do you remember that forgiveness that Sam had offered to John Dunnigan about 60 seconds ago? Satan, the enemy of our soul, was whispering in Sam's ear, "Do you really mean it? Can you walk your talk?"

Sam realized he was under the enemy's attack and answered his new friend John by saying, "God has something great for me, but he has not opened that door yet. I am praying and standing in faith that I will always be within God's will, no matter where I work."

"Just remember, God will never fail you. Even when we fail Him, He never fails us. May God bless you in the days ahead as you find a new job," Mr. Dunnigan said, delivered in a tone that Sam associated with the man from the meetings. The "church buddy on the beach," first name basis casual conversation, ended as quickly as it had begun.

Sam Sullivan, newly baptized Christian, had just

successfully passed one of the tests of faith. He could have blasted John Dunnigan because he lost his job.

The two roommates had a blessed afternoon, watching several of their friends being baptized. Afterward several of the men had fellowship together. Sam was so thankful for the new friendships he had developed with other men at Fellowship Church in just a few weeks.

"Well brother," Russ said in his usual upbeat style of speech as they drove home late that afternoon, "you are now a baptized believer, but tomorrow you and I need to get back to the job searches before the repo man comes for both of our cars."

Both men knew how easy it was to become complacent during a time of unemployment, so they encouraged each other and also became accountable to each other, not only for spiritual matters, but also for their job searches. Neither one would allow the other to become lazy. Each evening sitting across the table from each other they would share what efforts they had made that day in seeking employment. They helped each other with resumes. They took phone messages for each other when potential jobs called back, always being very careful to present the best possible image to a prospective employer. As you can imagine, those accountability sessions over the job searches were also bathed in apartment 111 prayer.

"God has a plan and a purpose. We just have to stay in His will until it is revealed to us," Russ often reminded Sam.

Each afternoon one of the two men would go to the apartment mailbox and pull out that day's mail. There was usually a couple of bills, a bundle of ads and often something from their church or from a ministry that would encourage them. Once in a while Sam would receive legal paperwork from Becky's attorney, now that they were headed to court shortly.

On Thursday following the baptism, Russ picked up the mail. That day it was 100% advertisements. After a sort through them, looking for discount fast food coupons, Russ tossed the entire stack of mail into the kitchen trash can.

That evening at their accountability session, in addition to their spiritual walks and their job searches, the two men also prayed about their finances. Russ had nothing and Sam's resources were quickly being exhausted between his own minimal expenses in addition to the weekly checks to his family.

Sam, being the former banker, had to list out the expenses versus what they had available. As you can imagine of these two men, from what little income they did have from incidental resources, God's tithe was the first 10% removed and set aside for Sunday, regardless of what else had to be paid that week.

As Russ explained to Sam, "It's all God's money and He is allowing us to use 90% if we give him back 10%. To steal from the tithe would be worse than stealing from that bank where you used to work."

"Amen, brother." Sam was even beginning to talk like his new friend and roommate.

When they got up from the table, Sam tore off the piece of paper he had been figuring on. Walking across the kitchen, he bounced the rolled up paper off the wall behind the wastebasket. It missed the basket and fell on the floor. Sam bent over to pick it up and put it in the basket. As he did, he noticed the edge of a return envelope from the bank where he used to be employed. He had seen their logo for enough years to recognize it from even the smallest part.

Curious as to what it was, Sam pulled it from the trash can and discovered it not to be an ad, but a personal envelope addressed to him. Sam had severed all relationships with the bank and could not understand who would be writing him. He tore open the envelope out of curiosity and saw that it contained a one-page letter addressed to him. Instinctively, he went to the signature and saw one word; "John." Above and below the one word signature was the name and title of John Dunnigan, President of the bank where Sam had once worked.

Sam went back to the top of the letter and began to read. It was addressed to, "Dear Sam." After reading only a few seconds he let out such a scream that Russ came running from the kitchen to see what was wrong.

Sam was sitting at the kitchen table and he was literally gasping for breath. His eyes were big, and the hand holding the letter was trembling. The first words out of Sam's mouth were a testimony to his dependence on God.

"Praise the Lord, praise the Lord, God is so good. He gets the glory!"

Russ moved around behind Sam's chair to read over his shoulder and see what could be in that letter, evoking such a response.

John Dunnigan wrote that after meeting Sam on Sunday at the baptismal, he was interested in the circumstances leading to Sam's termination and began to look into the matter. Apparently Sam had been picked out to be terminated because another officer on the same level, who should have been booted, was involved in an affair with a coworker, to allow them to keep working together, Sam was terminated.

Mr. Dunnigan wrote about how he had done "personal housecleaning" in that area of the bank and as a result, they had an opening for an officer in the position Sam had been dismissed from months before. The letter went on that Mr. Dunnigan had instructed the bank's Human Resources Department to reinstate Sam at his salary from before and his seniority and benefits were to continue as if he had never been gone. The letter continued that Mr. Dunnigan had discovered that Sam's office was being used as a private room for the two people involved in the illicit relationship to make and receive their phone calls.

Not only was Sam being invited to return to the bank, he would be returning to the same office as before.

Sam's normally light complexion was even lighter as he sat in that chair, blood drained from his face, praising the Lord. Russ, as you can imagine, whooped and hollered through the entire apartment.

On Friday, Sam called Human Resources and discovered everything was set up for his return, just as the letter had expressed. Three days later, on Monday, Sam Sullivan would once again be a banker.

Russ was so apologetic to Sam for throwing out his letter, thinking it was junk mail. "I'm pretty glad you're a bad basketball player and missed when you shot that piece of paper at the trash can. Do you realize that if you had hit the can, you would have had no reason to bend over and you never would have seen that letter? The bank would assume that you were not interested in your old job and would have given it to someone else."

Russ was as thrilled for Sam as if he had been recalled to his own IT job. On Saturday Russ carefully detailed Sam's BMW under the same tree where Sam had been led to the Lord several weeks prior. He wanted his Christian brother to look like a banker when he pulled into the bank parking lot on Monday morning.

That Sunday at church was a special time of rejoicing in praise for those two guys, thankful to God for His timing in this miracle. They brought in the tithe, which was about to increase drastically and you will not be surprised to hear that each man, now with more faith that ever, saved a seat at church for his wife.

As the old hymn reminds us, *"It is no secret what God can do, what He's done for others, He'll do for you."* On Monday we will soon see a man who never thought he would be a banker again, return to his bank with everything just as it was before. Should we not soon expect to see this same man who never thought he would be a husband again, return to his family with everything just as it was before? God heals hurting families.

Chapter 20

God Bless The Dragon

Monday, Sam's first day back at the bank, was great. Even though he had a stack of memos to read and catch up on from the months he had been gone, Sam was amazed at how quickly he fell back into the routine. He was encouraged by the warm welcome he received from his co-workers. By that afternoon, Sam was already making decisions and carrying out the work of a banker.

Off and on all day Sam had thought how he would let his wife know that the bank had rehired him. The restraining order that Becky's attorney insisted on extending, did not allow for direct contact. Normally, he would have told his attorney, who would have told her attorney, who would have sent Becky a letter. But Sam did not want the good news he had for his wife to be disclosed in a letter that began, *"Please be advised that... ."*

Sam could have called the Tomlinsons and asked his next-door neighbors to give Becky the good news, but this just seemed too personal for the neighbors to hear before his own wife.

By late afternoon, Sam had reached a decision. That evening he would risk sending Becky an email for the first time since he left home.

"I know my wife, and I really can't imagine her running to her attorney when I am emailing to tell her the check I send each week will drastically increase," Sam reasoned.

He knew that such an email would have to be brief and

beyond that, it absolutely could not contain even a hint of endearment.

Russ was out at a church function when Sam arrived home from work. The first thing Sam wanted to do was to send that email to his wife. Russ, being a computer guy, had all the latest equipment, so Sam sat down at Russ' computer to compose his email. He reasoned that if he dictated it, perhaps it would come across in the way he desired, so he activated Russ' Dragon voice activation system, went into his own email account and began to speak.

"Becky,

Please forgive me for contacting you directly, but I had good news affecting you that I did not want to send via the attorney-to-attorney-to-you system. I have been rehired by the bank as of today. The weekly checks you and the kids receive from me will triple as of Friday. Again, please forgive me for notifying you in this manner. It will not happen again.

Sam"

Sam stared at the screen and reread his short message several times to make certain there was nothing in there that could be misconstrued by his wife.

While he was reading for the final time and with his finger poised above the "Send" key, jovial Russ came bouncing into the apartment.

"Hey brother, how was your first day back at the bank? I never dreamed I would have a big-time banker for a roommate."

Sam turned to his roommate and began to describe his

day at the bank. Unfortunately, or fortunately, depending on whose view you take, Sam also forgot to deactivate the Dragon. Every word he spoke was being typed into Becky's email, unedited without his realizing it.

hey brother my day was great it was almost as if I had never been gone john dunigan even called to check that I was getting settled you know what was different today it was the way to look at my coworkers and the customers I had contact with no longer are they pawns for me to use in this chess game called banking I see them as souls of people who hurt as people would need Jesus just as you shared with me you know what was different today was that each time the secretary called mr sullivan you have a call on line whatever I knew it would not be my becky I am emailing her right now just to let her know the checks will increase I do not want her worrying all week about finances yes I know I risk going to jail for writing her but if you knew my becky and some day you'll get to meet her you will see how precious she is I made the mistake of getting so wrapped up in my career that I forgot my wife and kids almost I would go home and unload a days worth of frustration on her when she never deserved it God forgive me for what I did I only pray someday he will give me the opportunity to try with his help to be a husband again only this time a decent husband yes I could get on with my life as the attorney tells me with somebody else but no matter what I would not stop loving my precious becky my kids need me and my wife needs me now that my career has been restored I am praying that my marriage will be restored next are you ready for devotions I am done here let me send this and I will be right there

With that, Sam tapped the Send key on this computer he was not familiar with. Unbeknownst to Sam, his side of the entire conversation had just been sent to Becky! He did not realize what had happened.

Mid-morning Tuesday Sam was busy with bank activities when his secretary called on the intercom. "Mr. Sullivan, your wife is on line four."

Isn't it odd how satan always attempts to convince us of the dark side of any situation? God is doing something good, and the enemy just can't stand it. Sam placed his hand on the receiver, not wanting to pick up the phone.

He was certain it was going to be Sandy, the nurse he had lived with for a short time. Sam suspected that, even though it had only been a day and a half, she had heard that he was back at the bank in a good paying position and now wanted to collect palimony or something.

Sam prayed that God would give him wisdom in this situation as he picked up the phone and with a voice of authority and confidence said his name.

"Sam this is your wife, Becky... ."

You could have knocked Sam over with a feather. Not only was Becky prohibited by court order from calling him, the attorney had assured Sam what little interest Becky ever had in him as a husband was gone. Becky was probably the last person on earth Sam was expecting to hear from that day. He sat frozen, unsure what to say or how to respond.

"Sam this is your wife Becky," his wife repeated. "Did you hear me?"

"Yes.., yes, I did," Sam replied. Sam thought instantly that Becky was calling in response to his email from the night before that he should not have sent.

Did you ever notice that when God is at work, satan stays

at work also? Even when we have His promise that God will prevail, the devil will not give up. Even then, the evil one was running scenarios through Sam's head. He imagined her calling to say there was a warrant out for his arrest because the email to her was in violation of the restraining order. Maybe something serious had happened to one of their three kids. Regardless of why she was calling, Sam did not expect it to be good news.

Becky began, "I know I'm not supposed to call you, but if you can send an email like you did last night, I think I'm entitled to one phone call to even the score."

In 14 years of marriage, Sam knew his wife pretty well. He had not learned how to cherish her as a wife as God instructs, but Sam had learned Becky's traits quite well. He was a little confused that her comment about his email was delivered with the certain frivolity with which she made jokes. Sam was thankful that maybe he wasn't going to be hauled off to jail on his second day back on the job at the bank.

"Sam, honey, I.., I don't even know where to begin. The email you sent me last night was the most beautiful thing I've ever seen from you in my entire life. I can't get over it. Most of the night I was awake crying and just wondering where we went wrong. Oh, Sam, please forgive me for failing you as a wife. Please, please will you forgive me?"

That dignified banker, sitting in his fancy glass office and wearing his expensive suit, must have looked odd to anyone watching him. He had been leaning back in his chair, with a perplexed look on his face, phone in one hand and the other hand scratching his head trying to decipher what in the world his wife was talking about, but Sam's odd appearance was just beginning.

"I'm so glad you're pleased that the money is going to increase. I know it's been rough on you and the kids, but this should make it better," Sam said.

Unbeknownst to Sam, Becky was about to drop the bomb.

"Honey, all that would make life better for us is to have you back at home, living as a family. I know we would have a lot of work to do, but I know we can do it."

Sam responded with the only thing that came to his mind. "You know we're not supposed to be talking to each other, with the restraining order and all."

Becky might not have heard his comment because she went right on full steam.

"Sammy, I've made a discovery of what we need to succeed as a family. I failed you so much in our marriage, but even greater than that, I failed God. But now that is all straightened out, and I am standing and praying for God to restore our marriage. He can do it. I have that much faith.

"Sammy, the money doesn't even matter. What you wrote about me touched me more than you will ever know, especially because you never knew you were writing it. God allowed me to look inside your heart, to see the real Sam, the man I fell in love with, the man I married."

Instantly, God revealed to Sam Sullivan what he had done. The Dragon voice activation had been on while Sam described his first day back at work to his roommate. He sent a transcript of his first-day-back-at-the-bank report to Becky without even being aware of it.

If you would have been watching Sam, looking puzzled and scratching his head, and leaning back in his chair, you would have enjoyed what happened next.

The color drained from his face almost totally and his mouth fell open. His eyes got big and the hand that had been scratching his head suddenly fell to his side. Sam realized that everything he had told his roommate had been sent by accident to his wife! Sam attempted to recall what he had written.

Actually Sam was attempting to recall what he had said to Russ with the Dragon system activated. He knew what he had written, which was most impersonal. What he had said was quite personal.

Sam Sullivan, the banker, could dance out of almost any situation, except for this one. He sat in silence and did not know what to say.

"Honey, I am tired of being hustled through the legal system. All I hear is sign this paper, read this, you are going to go to court and this is going to happen. It all stops today! I'm going to go see my attorney and demand that things be done my way, and not his any longer. Sam, I can promise you, by the help of God, we will never be divorced, at least not at my hand. How we straighten all this mess out, I do not know, but for my part I am praying and trusting God to do it.

"Sammy, I have to run to get to that final attorney appointment, but just know that I love you today more than I ever did. You just hang on for a while and I will get the mess I have made unscrambled. Bye, hon."

Sam heard a dial tone in his ear. Becky had hung up knowing it would be difficult for Sam to know what to say in response. As he listened to the dial tone in his ear, Sam wondered if he could be dreaming or something. He thought maybe someone was playing a nasty trick on him, but no one could replicate that one-flesh relationship between Sam and Becky enough to pretend to be his wife.

Sam headed for the executive washroom. He locked the door behind him and got down on his knees in thankful prayer to God. What he had been praying for and trusting God for was in the birthing stage. His marriage was going to be restored to the glory of God.

Becky had not even given Sam time for him to ask about her relationship to Christ, but there was something there that can only come from God. Sam asked God to give Becky wisdom and strength in the meeting with her attorney that she was about to attend.

Neither the dirtiness of that floor, nor its hardness on his knees, nor the damage to his expensive suit mattered one ounce to Sam Sullivan. He knew there was quite a journey between that restroom and home just a few miles to the north, but God had started the process of restoration for the Sullivan family.

To God be the glory, great things He has done.

Chapter 21

Outside Of Fort Pierce

"Mr. Sullivan," Sam's secretary announced. "Doug Tomlinson from Tomlinson Insurance is waiting on line five for you. Do you wish to take his call on a personal matter?"

Sam had not talked to his next-door neighbor, Doug, for quite some time. Sam recalled the last time as being their 30 minute conversation, on a Saturday, in the parking lot at McDonald's, just before Sam accepted Christ that same day.

Sam assumed the Tomlinsons had sided with Becky in the divorce mess and were shying away from him. He was about to be proven wrong.

"Sam Sullivan," Sam said as he picked up the telephone. He was surprised at the cheery way Doug Tomlinson replied.

"Hey buddy, how are you doing? I think about you often, I just don't get around to calling you. By the way, congratulations on being back at the bank. I know that is truly your first love."

"I'm doing great, just great," Sam said in response. "But may I correct you on something? This bank is really my third love now. First comes the Lord, second comes my family and then comes banking. You know, for years I had those top three all in the wrong order. Actually I guess there were only two of the three that I would pay attention to at all. For 14 years the bank has come first and my family would get what was left of me. Somehow I associated a good paycheck and regular promotions with success, not a happy family."

Doug replied, "Sam, please do not think it was at your expense, but Susan and I have really looked carefully at our own marriage since you guys have been having struggles."

Sam was encouraged by his next-door neighbor's "having struggles" comment. He could have rightfully said, "... since you guys are getting divorced."

"The purpose of my call," Doug continued, "is to give you an invitation. Do you remember the cottage that we have in Georgia? Since you're by yourself I thought maybe you'd like to drive up on Friday night and spend the weekend there. It's not much but it's quiet, and you'll have a place to talk to the Lord. I always feel so refreshed when we come back from there. I can be gone for two days and feel like I have been gone two weeks. The lake is beautiful at this time of year. How about it, buddy? Would you accept my invitation?"

Sam replied by telling Doug about some of his memories from the times they had been up there as families. Much like his neighbor, Sam always came home feeling like a new man. He could not imagine what it would be like up there alone now that he was a Christian. He gladly accepted the invitation.

Doug told Sam where the door key was hidden and a couple of other necessary facts he would need to enjoy his mini-vacation in Georgia. Sam could hardly wait for Friday to arrive.

God promises us that He will never put more on us than He puts in us to bear, but even the best of Christians have bad weeks for any number of reasons. For Sam, this week had been uphill all the way with challenges he'd had at work. He and Russ had a minor squabble, which was quickly resolved with prayer, but nevertheless it took a toll on Sam. Above all else, Sam was disappointed that Becky had not called him again. Thursday night, he was awake most of the night feeling guilty about getting ready to go away for a holiday weekend that his family would not enjoy.

Friday morning before work, a bleary-eyed Sam loaded a few belongings into a suitcase and said goodbye to the still-unemployed Russ. That last business day of the week at the bank was a continuation of what Sam had experienced all week long. It was a nightmare, but he now had a new source of strength, Jesus, to help bear his problems.

About 4:45 P.M. on that Friday afternoon, Sam had an idea and called apartment 111. Russ answered in his usual jovial voice. Sam invited him to go to Georgia to the cottage with him for the weekend.

"I am wiped out and you can help me drive and stay awake. How about going to a cottage in Georgia for the weekend?" Sam invited. Somewhere deep within, Sam must have thought this would help make up for the small rift the two men had experienced earlier in the week.

"Brother," Russ spoke with an air of disappointment. "You are breaking my heart. I have never driven that BMW of yours and would welcome the opportunity. Being on a lake at a cottage all weekend sounds great. Unfortunately, one of the brothers from our Bible study, who is also unemployed, had his brakes go out. I promised to help him fix them tomorrow."

"I didn't know you could repair cars."

"I can't," Russ replied, "but I can sure hand tools and pray for them while the other guys do it. Anyhow, thanks for the invite and you have a blessed time. See you in a few days."

At 5 P.M. sharp, Sam endured the traffic leaving downtown Fort Lauderdale and headed west to the Florida Turnpike. Sam was more refreshed and relaxed than he thought he would be. The praise music coming from the same CD system that once played worldly music soothed his soul.

Do you know what occupied Sam's thoughts as he drove? In days past, it probably would have been something coming up at the bank or something that he wanted to buy. Has this man ever changed! On Friday evening, driving alone, he thought about his family. Sam thought about what kind of a Christian he was being. Sam prayed for more things than you can imagine. Once when a car came driving by him recklessly, Sam even prayed for the protection of that driver.

Shortly after 8 P.M. Sam stopped at the YeeHaw Junction service plaza on the Turnpike for dinner. It bothered him that almost everyone else was with a loved one and here he was going off for a holiday weekend by himself. For just a few minutes, Sam allowed satan to attempt to ruin his getaway. It was only after talking with the truck driver, who was also alone in Burger King and hearing from that stranger how lonely he was without his family, that Sam got his thinking back into the correct perspective.

It was almost 11:30 P.M. when a very tired Sam Sullivan crossed the Georgia line and prepared to exit two miles ahead. He had been a guest with his family at the Tomlinson's cottage enough times to know the directions by heart. It suddenly dawned on Sam that he was going to be there all alone for a couple days. There would be no Russ bouncing in and out, no hope of running into his family in Fort Lauderdale, just him and Jesus in that small cottage. Sam determined as he headed west to make this weekend one that would long stand out in his spiritual history.

As Sam exited the paved road and drove down the gravel drive, he rounded a curve and imagined that he saw a light on inside the Tomlinson cottage, far ahead of him. In about 30 seconds, Sam was aware there was a car sitting in front of the cottage. He suspected there were burglars in the cottage and had picked up his cell phone, ready to call 911. He slowly pulled closer to get a better look.

To say that Sam was shocked at what he saw is an understatement. The car sitting in front of the cottage was Becky's! He did not know what to do. He considered turning right around and heading back to Fort Lauderdale, but that would keep him up all night and he was tired. There was also the option of going to a South Georgia hotel and then going home Saturday morning. Sam could not imagine how the Tomlinsons could make the mistake of inviting both him and his estranged wife to the cottage on the same weekend.

Actually, it was not a mistake. It was a carefully concocted plan by Susan and Doug, owners of the cottage. They wanted their neighbors back together so very badly, but there was a restraining order in place. The Tomlinsons mistakenly calculated that the Florida restraining order would not be valid two miles into Georgia. Little did they know that the Violence Against Women Act, a federal law, provided "full faith and credit" for the Florida restraining order in all states. They were unknowingly setting Sam and Becky up to be in contempt of court, if anyone should make an issue of them being together.

Susan had worked with Becky to give her an invitation to the cottage and then Doug had done the same with Sam. The Tomlinsons would not be needing the cottage this weekend. Not only did they have the kids, they had become serious about praying for marriage restoration for this family, fractured by satan because of the future ability they had to accomplish much for the cause of Christ.

As Sam turned off his headlights, sitting on the narrow rock road, pondering what to do, his mind flashed back to the nights of being a repo man, when he and Jerry spotted the car they were seeking and then prepared to legally steal it.

Suddenly the porch light on the cottage came on, the front door opened and Becky walked out to see if she had heard a car. Seeing his wife standing on that porch he realized she was more beautiful than Sam had ever seen her before. Chills went through his body. What should he do?

It suddenly came to Sam that he was still a repo man. He was here, with God's help, to repossess the marriage that satan had attempted to steal. Sam turned on his headlights and pulled into the cottage.

Sam will now tell you that in about five seconds he saw his beautiful wife's expression change from fear to recognition, from shock to joy. Our brother knew that above everything else, Jesus had to be in control of what was about to happen. Sam could not rush things. He had to let Jesus move.

With Becky still standing on the porch, now with her mouth open in amazement, Sam exited his car and stood by the opened vehicle door. Neither one wanted to be the first to speak. Finally Sam broke the silence.

"Honey, please believe me that I did not follow you here. I swear I did not." Sam explained how Doug had called and offered him the use of the cottage for this weekend.

A shocked Becky then told how Susan had offered her the cottage for the same weekend.

Suddenly the one-flesh relationship between these two kicked in and they realized they had been set up! They did not know whether to laugh or to get angry.

"I could just go to a hotel," Sam offered, "and then drive home tomorrow. I do not want to ruin your weekend."

Becky's reply is one Sam will never forget.

"The only way you will ruin my weekend is to see you get in the car and drive away."

In about two leaps Sam was on the porch of that rustic cottage, with his wife in his arms for the first time in many months. They hugged and sobbed and kissed and sobbed. Even though it was only for about five minutes, both of them thought they had stood there for hours. Both of them were oblivious to the South Georgia bugs the porch light had attracted, that were swarming around them.

Sam did not even bother unpacking. They went inside and talked as husband and wife and this lasted for hours. If you had to identify a specific time of reconciliation for the Sullivans, it had just taken place on that front porch. There was still a lot of work to be done toward restoration, but the process began on that front porch that night.

Saturday morning Sam and Becky both slept in. When he woke up, he could not believe he was with his wife. When she woke up she could not believe she was with her husband. That morning they both talked again.

In the future, this couple would relate often about the doughnut incident. On her way out to the cabin, Becky had purchased a dozen doughnuts for the weekend. For some strange reason when she had selected her doughnuts, Becky had asked for three coconut doughnuts. These were Sam's favorites, but she could not stand the taste of them. Just a few minutes before her husband had arrived on that Friday night, Becky had looked in the box to get herself a bedtime doughnut and could not imagine why she had purchased three coconut doughnuts. God loved this couple so much that He had even arranged for Becky to have her husband's favorite breakfast for him, right out there in the woods.

It was amazing how the Lord had been leading their lives, separately but going in the same direction.

"Honey," Sam offered, "do you know that spot just south of Stuart where I-95 and the turnpike parallel each other? For several miles it looks like they're all one road, but then I-95 heads off to the west. In Fort Pierce both roads come back together again. It seems like God has been carrying us, separately, but in the same direction."

"If Susan and Doug ever look for a name for this place, I suggest Fort Pierce," Susan offered.

That afternoon, Becky was going to be thrilled when she walked out from the cottage and saw the torn off lid from a cardboard box tacked on the frame of the porch. Her husband had written "Fort Pierce," going over and over the same letters many times with a ball point pen to make them stand out. This is just like something he would do.

Maybe not yet legally, but emotionally and spiritually Becky had her Sam back. To God be the glory!

Chapter 22

It's A Small World

Do you know the song that every child leaves Disney World singing? The catchy little tune tells about *"It's a small world after all,"* and ends with, *"It's a small, small world."* Sam and Becky are about to discover what a small world they live in. Actually, they did not discover what a small world it is, as much as they discovered what a big God we have.

Saturday afternoon at the cottage Sam and Becky were doing what they had been doing for most of the weekend. They were talking. This time they were sitting on the front porch swing. The low rumble of the sound of gravel being compressed by vehicle tires became louder as a car approached. As a beautiful black Lexus drove past where they were sitting, the couple in the car both waved at the Sullivans. Sam and Becky returned the wave. The only people who traveled that dead end road were residents, so everyone seemed to know one another.

The Lexus had only gone a few feet past the cottage when it suddenly stopped. The backup lights came on, and the car reversed to be even with Sam and Becky. The passenger side window came down and the male driver shouted across the female sitting in the front seat with him.

"Sam, we keep running into each other in the strangest places, my brother."

Outside Fort Pierce must be a place for surprises. That car was being driven by John Dunnigan, the president of Sam's bank. Sam had last talked to Mr. Dunnigan at the baptism.

Sam got up from the porch swing and started out for the road. He suddenly recalled the Dunnigans owned a cottage down the road from the Tomlinsons. These two families, who traveled in a social circle well above the Sullivans, had purchased their cottages at the same time. Sam had never seen the Dunnigans there during any of his previous visits.

As Sam started for the Lexus, Becky caught up with him and held his hand as they walked together.

"Hello, Mr. Dunnigan," Sam greeted.

"Sam, please remember, it's John outside the bank."

"I'm very sorry. I just didn't want to be inappropriate."

John Dunnigan continued, "Sam, this is my wife, Bonnie."

Becky continued to hold onto her husband's hand as she was introduced to John Dunnigan. She knew the name and his title, but she had no idea how her husband had gotten on a first name basis with the president of his bank.

"I see something I like," John Dunnigan said. "An employee who honors his wife. We have so many upper-level people going through divorce, people who put job before family, that it was refreshing for me to see you two walking out here holding hands."

What do you say at a time like that? Do you come clean and tell the man you haven't seen your wife for months until the night before? Do you tell him that you are among the upper level people headed for divorce? Fortunately, John Dunnigan spoke before Sam had to do either.

"Bonnie and I are driving into Valdosta tonight to our favorite spaghetti place for dinner. Would you two care to join us? We would like to get to know both of you."

Becky gave Sam's hand a little squeeze and at the same time delivered a half smile and slight nod. After 14 years of marriage, Sam knew this was Becky's approval to say yes to the invitation.

"We would be honored to have dinner with you," Sam replied.

"Could we pick you up about 6:30 P.M.?" John asked.

"That would be great. We're looking forward to it."

Sam was both surprised and very pleased that his wife exchanged small talk with Bonnie Dunnigan. Even on a very brief first meeting, it seemed that Bonnie and Becky connected, even though there were many years difference in their ages.

As the Dunnigans pulled away, Sam and Becky stood by the side of the road. Having the prez give a greeting to you at your baptism and going to dinner with him and his wife were miles apart. Suddenly Sam felt that he was in over his head on a couple of things this weekend.

With a serious look on his face, Sam asked his wife, "Honey, what in the world do we do?"

Becky never released Sam's hand as she looked him straight in the face and said, "We thank God for the opportunity to go to dinner with your big boss and his wife, and we go and have a great time."

Sam was not as settled as was his wife. "We can't go with them and pretend to be Ozzie and Harriet, when in fact, if we drive two miles south there is a restraining order in effect. Becky, I can't use you to advance my career at the bank. Every guy on my floor would give his right arm to be going out socially with Dunnigan. Hon, I just can't use you like that."

Sam was fully confident that they were on the road to marriage restoration, but this was just all too soon. Becky's words reassured him.

"You are not using me. What's yours is mine and what's mine is yours. I would be honored to be on the arm of a banker going to dinner with the president of his bank. The Dunnigans seem like nice people and I'm sure we will have a great time. Just forget that you even work in the same place."

Becky's sweetness that all the events of recent months had attempted to erase was back. Sam smiled, knowing that his wife, his family and his marriage were being returned to him.

That afternoon Sam and Becky prayed together for probably the first time in their lives. They shared how each had come to Christ. Becky laughed about the week at church when she had responded to the invitation, walking within six feet of her husband and never seeing him.

Sam shared some deep secrets from their time of separation and asked for forgiveness. Becky had not intended to disclose the school teacher incident, but how could she forgive her husband for something as simple as the things he had confessed when she was harboring an actual date? God led her to tell Sam the entire school teacher story.

This husband and wife forgave each other for anything that had happened during their separation. Together in prayer they forgave their daughter, Connie for the 911 call that put so much into motion. Sam would later say that was one of the best afternoons of his life.

Even though Becky thought that she was only coming to a cottage where no one would see her all weekend, for some odd reason Becky had brought a casual dress-up outfit with her. For Sam, like most men, it was easy to grab a pair of slacks and a shirt that made him look like a million dollars.

They did one other thing that afternoon. They called and spoke with their kids and they spoke with the Tomlinsons. Doug and Susan had been praying for about 24 hours that everything would go well between this fractured couple. All four had a laugh at how Sam and Becky both discovered they were coming to the same cottage for a weekend alone.

Sam told how they were going out to dinner with the Dunnigans and how they looked forward to that evening.

After hanging up the phone, Susan looked at her husband and said, "We have a lot to thank God for because we took quite a chance to get them out of state together, but it worked."

Doug quickly added, "And it sounds like John and Bonnie got our message."

That evening at 6:30 P.M. the Dunnigans stopped by to pick up Sam and Becky. When that black Lexus pulled in, John was driving and Bonnie was in the backseat. It was quite obvious to Sam that he was supposed to get in the front seat with John. Bonnie and Becky sat in the back and as women often do, they were immediately engrossed in conversation. In the front seat, Sam was on guard, to say the least.

The day before he was at work at this man's bank, never suspecting that on Saturday night he would be riding along with their wives in South Georgia on the way out to dinner. Sam silently told himself that if God ever allowed him to be totally successful in banking, he wanted a black Lexus. Never had he ridden in a car as smooth as this one. It could have been just that Sam was floating on air, going out to dinner with the big boss.

Sam discovered that John was a man, just like him. They talked very little banking, but they talked sports, politics, Fellowship Church, the Christian faith and so much more. By the time they arrived at the spaghetti restaurant which was the Dunnigan's favorite place to eat in Valdosta, Sam had relaxed and almost forgotten the stature of the man he was with.

The two couples sat at a round table. The position of John Dunnigan apparently had not been overlooked by the staff of that restaurant. Sam had never been treated so well at any meal as the service they received that night. He had always imagined John Dunnigan eating steak at every meal. On that Saturday night, both John and his wife ordered lasagna.

After they had ordered, John said, "So tell me about this Sam Sullivan and his wife. What makes them tick?"

Sam began with some formalities of his education, how long he had lived in Fort Lauderdale, how long he had been at the bank, and how he and Becky had met. His wife joined in telling about their children and her being a stay-at-home mom, and a couple of her activities in the community.

John had been listening intently to the words spoken by Sam and Becky. After Sam had finished speaking, John sat with his chin poised on his hand, as if expecting to hear more.

Sam could take this cat and mouse game no longer. "Mr. Dunnigan, I mean John, there really is a lot more to our story that I think you deserve to hear, sir."

John Dunnigan sat as though frozen, not saying a word.

Sam gave his wife's hand a squeeze on top of the table and she gave him one of her affirming smiles and nods. With that, Sam began to unload, starting with the 911 call.

What details he forgot Becky filled in, from her vomiting on the street in front of the courthouse, to the flowers from Cincinnati, to the school teacher incident. The Sullivans talked as if they had finally found people who cared about their marriage.

Sam told how he was led to the Lord by a guy whose car he had helped repossess and how he was now the roommate of that personable IT guy. Becky told of the card she received at Skyline and how she had given her heart to the Lord at Fellowship Church.

The food was served, but no one started eating. As Becky talked, Sam knew just how much he did love her. He shared about his growth as a Christian and how he had discovered that satan, not Becky, was the enemy.

After half an hour, Sam looked at the food getting cold and realized that he had probably said too much.

"I'm so sorry to keep us from eating. Please forgive me."

Becky could see a hint of tears in John Dunnigan's eyes while her husband was speaking. Finally he swallowed hard and began to talk.

"Sam, Becky, I feel that we owe you an apology. We knew part of your story before you ever told us. The Tomlinsons knew we were coming up this weekend and left a voice mail explaining your situation. They asked us to check in with you guys if we should see you. They were not sure if they were putting together a marriage or a bomb with the two of you in the same cottage for a weekend.

"I feel that we have deceived both of you by not being up front with what we knew. I guess the bank president in me was just curious if you would reveal anything at all about what was going on. I see remarkable traits in both of you, first as Christians and then as a couple with a successful marriage."

His next comment shocked Sam beyond belief.

"Sam, I admire and respect you, sir, for being open and honest. I see the traits in you that we look for when the bank needs another senior officer. Now if you will allow me to pray, we can eat this food that Sam caused to get cold." With that, he reached over and gave Sam a good-natured flick on the arm, not exactly what you would expect from a bank president.

When John prayed for their dinner, there was something in his prayer that both Sam and Becky picked up on. John asked God to give him and Bonnie wisdom and revelation knowledge in sharing their story to help this couple.

The Dunnigans must have been good customers at that restaurant because when they finished praying and were ready to eat, all of their food was served once again, not warmed over dishes, but all new food. The cold dishes disappeared before they could be touched.

Sam wondered what could possibly prompt such good service. Certainly it wasn't profitable, and their service surpassed any other table in the restaurant. It was almost a year later that Sam discovered that John Dunnigan owned that restaurant.

After a beautiful dinner, the two couples were having coffee and talking around the table. The evening was so relaxed and congenial that at times Sam forgot that the man sitting next to him was the president of the bank where he worked.

John Dunnigan developed quite a serious look. Sam's first thought was that the prez had indigestion from the Italian food. Once John started speaking, Sam knew differently.

"Sam and Becky, Bonnie and I appreciate the confidence you have placed in us tonight by telling us your story so openly. Foremost, you can be assured that we will be praying for both of you and for your children. You have taken us into your confidence and nothing you said will ever leave this room, except what we carry to God."

Sam and Becky knew from John's appearance that there was more to come. His mouth was slightly opened and he appeared as if the words just would not come out. After a few seconds he continued speaking.

"Bonnie and I want to tell you a story tonight. We are putting a lot on the line to share this. Sam, you are one of the few in our entire building who know any of this, so I am trusting you to keep it in the strictest of confidence."

Sam had an instant vision of him in grubby clothes, sitting in that repo truck again, dodging the verbal abuse and everything else that people often threw at them when their car was being picked up. Sam shuddered at the very thought of what he once did, and where he might end up again if fired from that bank. John Dunnigan could have confessed to being an axe murderer right then and Sam would have had amnesia. He did not know what they were about to hear was for his ears only.

"Many years ago," John began, "we were newlyweds and I was a teller at another bank. How madly in love we were with one another. Neither of us knew Christ, but we had a good marriage by the world's standards. After a couple of years of marriage and of banking, I received a small promotion. It was just enough to give me a secretary and a few extra dollars in my pocket. It also gave me an extremely big head. Feeling I was really something, combined with the secretary and some extra money, created problems.

"Suddenly Bonnie seemed dull and unattractive. Home life was a drag, but how I enjoyed coming to work and telling my secretary how bad life was at home. Sam, you can probably guess the rest of the story. I had an affair. It breaks my heart to this day to say it, but I was unfaithful to my new wife."

Bonnie chimed in, "I wasn't going to take it. As soon as the facts were disclosed I did everything all wrong. First, I ran to an attorney. I told everyone I knew what John had done. In every way I could, I attempted to take revenge. I saw John as my enemy and I was going to get even, one way or another. A woman I was working with at the school told me I should forgive him. I was so mad at her that I could have struck her. I did not want to forgive him. I wanted to physically attack him. I thought one way or another, John should be made to pay for all the hurt he had caused me.

"We were close to our court date," Bonnie continued, "and I was hurting so badly. I knew there had to be an answer. For some reason I don't even remember, I went to church one Sunday and heard one statement that rang in my head: "God heals hurting marriages." That morning at church I accepted Jesus Christ as my Savior. It did not come easy, but over time I was able to forgive John, forgive the other woman and to take a stand for my marriage. I was not going to let satan have what he was attempting to steal from our marriage."

John picked up the story at that point. "When this all came out at the bank, they fired both me and the secretary. In short order she was gone because I had caused her to lose her job. I spent four nights sleeping in my car in a public parking lot because Bonnie had frozen what small amount of money I had not squandered on the other woman. You know, Sam, any man who does what I did should be required to spend a few nights sleeping in his car. It certainly changes one's perspective and gives you a lot of time to think.

"I got a job driving a cab because it was quick cash, not much cash, but it was quick cash. At least I could afford a shabby room to sleep in. One day I picked up a man at the airport who was in town for a conference. He looked like an average businessman, well-dressed and articulate. We began a conversation about something on the way to his hotel on the beach. Somewhere on the 17th Street Causeway the man knew by the way I talked that I was something other than the average cab driver. He added that he suspected I had a college degree.

"The guy in the back seat of that cab was reading my mail. I thought I would never see him again, so I literally poured out my guts to him. I was hurting so badly and he was listening so well.

"When we pulled up to his hotel, he asked if I would leave the meter running and pull out of the way of the door for a couple of minutes. As hungry as I was, 'leave the meter running' was music to my ears, so I pulled into a cab slot.

The man was a pastor from Indiana and in town for a pastor's conference. He had once been a businessman, just like me, doing all the wrong things with all the wrong people.

"Pastor Tom Grant led me to the Lord, right there in a taxi, with the meter running, sitting in front of the Yankee Clipper Hotel. He took me to dinner that night and shared about what he and his wife, Julie had been through. She sounded so much like my Bonnie. I did not know much about praying, but Tom prayed that night for the restoration of our marriage and that Bonnie and Julie might be able to speak."

John Dunnigan suddenly stopped speaking. It was as if he felt that possibly he had already told too much.

"The rest is history. But Sam, if you are ever in my office, on top of the bookcase you will see a model taxi. That's my scar to remind me to never open the wound of marriage interruption again. Tom and Julie Grant are up in years now, but as my spiritual father he still keeps in touch with me.

"On that day in the taxi, Tom told me that when God restores a marriage, along with it comes the responsibility to share with others about marriage restoration as an alternative to divorce. So you see folks, God gave us no option but to share our story with you tonight."

By now the red napkins in that Italian restaurant were drying tears from four sets of eyes.

The drive back into the country in the dark was quite different than the drive into town. Sam felt as though he were sitting next to not his boss and bank president, but a friend and a Christian brother who really understood. It was almost as if it was Russ driving that car.

When they pulled up in front of the Tomlinson cottage, all four people got out of the car. John Dunnigan, a man who towered over Sam in size, gave him not a handshake but a sincere tight hug, as the two ladies also exchanged hugs.

Bonnie said, "John and I have a tradition when we are up here. We call it Fellowship Church North and have our Sunday devotions out on the deck overlooking the lake. Would you two care to join us tomorrow? We usually attend the 10 A.M. service."

This time Becky answered on behalf of Sam, "We would be honored. We'll be there at ten."

After the good nights were all said, Sam and Becky went into the cottage. They were up late that night talking and praying and planning their future together. They were both thankful to the Dunnigans, not for a meal, but for the message they shared from their hearts to help the Sullivans.

Sunday morning when Becky was first waking up, she imagined that her husband was rubbing her back like he did every morning when it was time to get up. In her grogginess, Becky thought she was dreaming, until she realized the nightmare for this family was over. Her husband really was rubbing her back.

Praise God.

Getting ready to go to Fellowship Church North at the Dunnigans, Becky asked what Sam wanted for breakfast. She laughed as she said, "About all I have to offer is a coconut doughnut" and both of them laughed at what God had done in having Becky buy something she didn't even eat.

The Dunnigan's cottage was hardly that. Just down the road and around another curve they discovered a beautiful lakefront home. Bonnie welcomed them inside and John came to greet them. All four walked out onto a beautiful deck that extended the entire length of the home. Bonnie had coffee and danish waiting on the table beside the four chairs. Sam and Becky shared the story of the coconut doughnuts. "Never be surprised at what God can do when we turn to Him and trust Him fully," John said.

The two couples had a beautiful time of fellowship, prayer and praise that morning. The Sullivans discovered that Bonnie had a beautiful voice. I wish you could have been there to see Sam and Becky holding hands, in a spirit of prayer, looking out on that lake, as Bonnie's voice echoed across the water, *"...Thy Kingdom come, Thy will be done...."*

At one point during prayer, Sam had prayed that his roommate, Russ, could find employment and that God would bring his wife home.

After their worship time together, the Dunnigans invited the Sullivans to stay for lunch.

"No, we could not impose on you anymore," Sam responded. "Please do not feel that you have to baby sit us for the sake of the Tomlinsons. We are on the right track now, thanks to God using people like you and the Tomlinsons."

John's reply shocked Sam and Becky. "Unless you have a pressing commitment and that's very doubtful out here in the woods, I'm going to insist that you stay. No one is babysitting you. Bonnie and I see so much of ourselves in you two.

"I want to tell you something else," John continued. "I hope this doesn't come out wrong, but knowing you guys, I think you'll understand. Bonnie and I lead a pretty lonely life, primarily because we have money. God has blessed us greatly above anything we could ever have imagined. Most of the people who want to be our 'friends' are either ten cent millionaires acting out a role or else they want something from us. It is so refreshing to fellowship with a Christian brother and sister who are just down to earth people ready to confess their struggles, but also ready to depend on God for their answers."

Neither Sam nor Becky knew how to respond. The Dunnigans basically owned the bank, and until recent days Sam had always thought of Dunnigan as a cold and distant person who manned the axe, ready to drop any bank position without notice. This weekend Sam and Becky had seen a Christian couple so successful, and yet they were lonely.

The two couples did have lunch together and talked openly once again about their marriage struggles.

"Tell me about Russ, the IT guy you prayed for this morning," John Dunnigan invited.

Sam told the story of going to repo Russ' car and finding it immaculate, with Russ ready to hand over the keys and registration. He continued to tell how he drove through the apartment complex on a Saturday a week later and saw Russ waxing his car and praying for someone to witness to.

"Does he have a resume?" John asked.

"Yes sir, he has a stack of them on our kitchen table," Sam replied.

For the first time, Becky wondered what her husband's dwelling away from home looked like.

John responded, "Now that you will be moving out, we had better find Russ a job, since you will not be there to help with the rent, nor to repo Russ' auto again." John Dunnigan laughed. It was the closest he could come to being funny.

"Again in confidence," John continued, "I have a project on the front burner I want to undertake, but God has not sent the right person to me. When I hear about a Christian brother from our church, who is decent enough to wax a car about to be repossessed, who is a soul winner and who took you under his wing, he sounds like the man I need. I am ready to put a lot of money into this project, but not until God sends the right person to head it up. We live in Sea Ranch Lakes. Do you think Russ might be available to drop off his resume to me on Monday at my home, even if it is a holiday?"

"Russ would walk on cut glass if there were a job on the other side. He wants so badly to demonstrate to his wife that he is successful. His self-esteem should be gone, but he looks to Christ and keeps on going and smiling just the same."

Addressing Becky, her husband added, "By the way, we almost had Russ spending the weekend with us. I called him Friday afternoon just before I left town and invited him, but he had promised one of the brothers from his Bible study, who also has no job, that he would help him fix the brakes on his car Saturday. I don't think things would have gone quite like they did if Russ had been with me do you, honey?"

Becky could not even imagine how the scenario would have played out if Russ had agreed to come. Being a new Christian, not even yet baptized, she had a serious question, "Do you mean that God does things like give people brake trouble just to carry out His will?"

"Not at all," John replied. "Evil comes from satan, the enemy of our souls. But everything that happens is filtered through the mighty hand of God. I do not know how to explain all of the theology, but if the brother had not been taking care of his brakes, he was destined to have brake trouble. God takes bad and turns it into good for His people. In this instance, when he wanted you two to be alone, he took what was already happening, the brake trouble, and turned it into an opportunity for us to serve. Just remember, Becky, all good things come from above."

In all sincerity, John made another attempt at humor. "I would have had all weekend to interview him though, because I think you guys would have had him staying down here, if you know what I mean."

That afternoon Sam and Becky said goodbye to the Dunnigans who now seemed like long time friends. They cleaned up the cottage and started back to Florida in two separate cars.

Southbound on I-75, Sam called Becky's cell phone just as they entered Florida.

"Am I at least 1000 feet behind you?" he chided.

“Honey, if you're 10 feet behind me you're too far away. My project for this week is to get the restraining order dropped,” Becky replied in love.

Sam followed his wife all the way down the turnpike. At an Orlando service area, they stopped for gas. Sam certainly was in contempt of court when he was pumping gas at Becky's car and leaned over and gave her a kiss.

This couple was getting brave. They ate dinner together at a service plaza restaurant, sitting in a booth next to a Florida Highway Patrol Trooper. Sam and Becky played footsies under the table.

“I'll never tell,” his beautiful bride responded.

On the way out of the plaza, Sam ran into the gift shop and bought three gifts. He handed them to Becky saying, “Tell the kids these are from daddy and he will be home real soon.”

Once back on the road, Sam had to call Russ and tell him the good news of the job possibility, not just a job, but a great job just as Russ had been seeking. The Lord was answering his prayers.

Becky called her husband's cell phone saying, “If you can kiss me at a service area, I guess I can call you on the phone.” The two talked until the cell phone batteries went dead.

To reach his apartment, Sam should have exited the Florida Turnpike at the Pompano Beach exit. Instead, always staying a thousand feet behind his wife, Sam followed Becky to the Sunrise Boulevard exit and then followed her East to Federal Highway.

If you were to ask Sam why he followed his wife, he would tell you it was to make sure Becky got home safely. There is a secondary reason. Sam wanted to just see their family home where he would soon be living once again. When Becky pulled into their driveway, Sam stopped short of their home by several houses. He sat there and observed his wife taking her weekend suitcase and the gifts out of the car.

Doug Tomlinson was coming around the corner of his house to roll a trash can out to the street. Just as he caught a view of Becky coming home next door she was blowing a kiss to someone down the street. When Doug reached the sidewalk, he saw Sam's black BMW backing away, not wanting to be seen driving by his home.

Doug went back inside his home and whispered to his wife, “Everything is all right with Sam and Becky.” Their prayers, along with the prayers of so many others, had been answered.

Please promise not to tell the judge what you've just read!

Chapter 23

Before The Judge

Following the Monday holiday, Sam walked into the bank Tuesday morning, floating on air. No, it was not due to him having spent part of the weekend with the bank's president. That was truly insignificant. That man walked into work floating on air because he had spent the weekend with his covenant wife.

As soon as the typical Tuesday, day after the holiday morning rush was over, Sam closed the door to his office and placed a call to the Broward County clerk of court to learn what was necessary in order for the restraining order Becky had against him to be dismissed. He heard that both he and Becky should come to that office and complete a civil drop charge statement. This would then be presented to the judge who would act upon it.

On that day Becky was going to call her attorney and make an appointment to have him start the dismissal proceedings. After enjoying the company of his wife for the past weekend, Sam wanted to go home just as soon as possible.

That day at lunch, Sam met Becky at the court clerk's office and completed the required form. Sam had written a statement to be attached to the form, explaining where he was coming from. Becky had done the same. They were told the form and their statements would be presented to the judge, who may dismiss the restraining order or may set the case for hearing. They were told this process could take as long as 10 to 14 days.

The clerk of court was most helpful in explaining to the Sullivans that since there was no actual physical violence, having the restraining order dismissed seemed not to be a problem. The clerk went on to remind Sam and Becky that until the restraining order was formally dismissed, it was still in effect.

Leaving the courthouse, Becky told Sam she sensed they should not see each other until they could do so legally. "Honey, I love you very much and do not want to risk having anything, anything at all stand in the way of our being together as a family."

Sam thought his wife was overreacting. After all, they had been together all weekend out of state and once back in Florida they had contact all the way home. Nevertheless, he was in agreement with his wife's wishes and they parted ways in front of the courthouse without any physical affection being shown.

Walking on the sidewalk on S.E. 6th Street, Becky passed the parking spot where she had parked months before when she went inside to obtain the restraining order. It really was not even needed, but Becky had been in shock. She did not know how to listen to Jesus, so she had to listen to other people. Their answers might have been wrong, but His are always 100% right.

Sam was not the only person walking on air in the building that day. As requested, Russ had dropped off his resume at Mr. Dunnigan's home in Sea Ranch Lakes on Monday.

Sea Ranch Lakes is not only a gated community, it is a walled community on the beach just north of Lauderdale-By-The-Sea. Russ never anticipated ever being behind those walls, much less welcomed in one of the homes. He had anticipated giving his resume to whoever answered the door. Fortunately, Russ had dressed well because John Dunnigan answered the door himself and invited Russ inside.

Their business relationship had to be ordained of God. John Dunnigan liked this man before he ever met him, based on what Sam had said in casual conversation the past weekend. Dunnigan was even more impressed once he met Russ in person and looked at his resume.

"Now that I think about it," Mr. Dunnigan said, "I remember seeing you with Sam on the day he was baptized. I have heard a lot this past weekend about the kind of man you are and the efforts you are making to disciple Sam in the ways of the Lord. I am impressed. Not many men would be where you are, unemployed and without your wife and still serving the Lord and his brothers with a joyful heart."

John Dunnigan made another one of his feeble attempts at humor. Fortunately he was a much better banker than he was a comedian. "I want to start a car waxing business, and I have been told you are the man for the job."

Russ could not understand what the man was talking about. He was an IT guy, not a car waxer. Wanting to impress this man so much, Russ did not know how to respond but got one of those goofy Russ looks on his face.

John Dunnigan was loving it. He let Russ squirm for about ten seconds and then he said, "I heard about the repo and the shiny car."

Russ was so relieved that he had not been invited here to apply for a job at a carwash that he said the first thing that came to mind, "Like I told Sam the night he came for my car,

I felt bad about not having money to meet that obligation, but every man has elbow grease he can invest into his debts."

John Dunnigan was a shrewd businessman, but at that point Russ could have just about named his salary and the date he wanted to start.

Russ was invited to sit with John in his office at home. John Dunnigan explained that he had interest in several businesses and had a burning desire to start another Christian business. His vision was to start a 100% Christian web hosting service. All that had been holding him back was finding the right man for the top.

"We both need to pray about this, but I sense in my spirit that you're the man that God has sent me for this project. Money is not my motive here. Of course I expect a straight profit, but more than that, I want us to serve the Lord through Christian web hosting," John Dunnigan told Russ.

"I've done a lot of research on this and I have some innovative ideas that you're going to tell me whether or not will work," he added.

"Sir," Russ replied, "I pray this does not come out as pious or self-righteous, but what you're describing is right where I am today. I have turned down jobs, good jobs, because my faith would not allow me to work in those environments. Last week I told Sam that it was sad that there was not a God's Way, an Internet for Christian people. The Lord has given us such a tool and the world is mis-using it so badly. I know so many marriages where satan has come in because of what one spouse, a Christian spouse, became involved with on the Internet. I pray that if it's God's will, He will allow you and I to work together to correct some of those things.

“I’m sorry, Mr. Dunnigan,” Russ apologized. “I got carried away with what you’re describing because it is close to my heart. Above all else, I want not just to be an IT guy, but a Christian IT guy.”

To say that Russ made a favorable first impression on John Dunnigan would be an understatement. The man absolutely loved him.

“Russ, you understand we'll have to go through the background checks, a drug test, and the usual hiring process, but I’m on the verge of offering you a job before somebody else does. I just can’t do that, do you understand?”

“Yes sir, I understand, but I would like to accept the position that you just did not offer me, regardless of the salary, working conditions, perks, or anything else. My foremost goals are to serve the Lord, to win back my wife and to make enough to live on.” One of those great big Russ smiles followed his statement.

John Dunnigan sensed that at some point in the future, he and Bonnie would be needing to share their story and confidence with another restored couple.

“Mr. Dunnigan, would I be out of place to ask if you and I can pray together about this?”

“Not at all sir, not at all.”

Those two men spent the next few minutes on their knees and holding hands at John Dunnigan's home office. Most people would be so intimidated by Mr. Dunnigan that they would not dare ask him to pray, but not Russ, the inventor of holy boldness. Not only did they pray, they clasped hands while they prayed.

John Dunnigan had hired and fired thousands of people in his career, but never had he been so certain on a first meeting that person was the right person, the only person, for the job.

After John saw Russ out the front door, John closed the door and leaned against it. "Thank you, Jesus for sending that man in my life."

As Russ left Sea Ranch Lakes, he really didn't need to head for the gates. That guy was so high in praising the Lord that he could have floated over the wall surrounding the community.

Prayer at apartment 111 was certainly different that Tuesday night. It was indeed a night of praise and thankfulness to God for all He had done in the lives of those two men. Sam was on the verge of having a restraining order lifted and being home with his family, and Russ was on the verge of a job that seemed to have been created by God just for him.

Did you know that when those two guys had their apartment 111 prayers they sang with the praise music playing in the background? It was as unto the Lord, because neither of them could come near to carrying a tune. Nevertheless, it must have pleased God that night that instead of them going out and celebrating what the world would call their "good fortune," they chose to praise the Lord.

The photos of their two wives sat in small frames on the kitchen table where they prayed. On that night Sam turned the picture of his wife down, saying, "One down and one to go. If our prayers got my job back, found you a job, got my wife saved and are bringing me back to my family, all that is left to intensify is the prayer for your wife. Man, I want to see you guys back together."

Wednesday morning Sam left for work and Russ started the first steps to becoming an employee of the Dunnigan Corporation. Both men were still praising God for all that He was doing.

Early Wednesday afternoon after returning from a bank meeting, Sam thumbed through his pink slip phone messages. One rose to the top to be called immediately. The clerk of court would like to talk to him. Sam was certain he was going to hear the restraining order had been dropped and he would be home that very night. What was told to him when he returned the call was not what he expected.

"Judge Bahnsen would like for you and your wife to appear before him at 9 A.M. next Monday in room 1404."

Sam was a disappointed man when he hung up the phone. He feared the judge was going to make an example out of them and refuse to drop the restraining order. Sam even wondered if Judge Bahnsen had something going on in his own life. Maybe there is a restraining order against him. Right away Sam thought about an appeal after next Monday morning.

At Becky's request, they had not been seeing each other nor communicating. After Sam hung up the phone on that Wednesday, he immediately broke the agreement and emailed Becky. Within two minutes she had replied, also by email.

"Sam I know, they called me also. Please pray because I am so worried what this means."

That evening at the apartment, Sam unpacked the things he had prepared to take home.

Have you ever been in a situation like Sam's? You are so certain that you know what God is going to do that when it doesn't go that way, you almost forget that God may be working another way. That's where Sam was that evening. For the first time in his short spiritual life, he did not attend Wednesday evening Bible study at his church, but instead stayed home and watched television, licking wounds and just certain that God had failed him.

When Russ came bouncing in from Bible study, unlocking the front door of the apartment with his Bible under his arm and humming a hymn, he saw Sam stretched out across the sofa.

"I missed you tonight, brother. Have to work late? Church was crowded and I had a heck of a time saving three extra seats. Wish you had been there." Russ sensed from the scowl on Sam's face and the fact that he appeared to have been watching television for quite a while, with his snacks on the floor beside him, that something was very wrong.

Apartment 111 was decorated in a style that we could call Early American Divorce. When Russ had first leased the apartment, he had no furniture. Several of his brothers at church had old furniture they gave him. With Sam lying across the sofa, the only option left was to plop his lanky frame into a worn-out and leaking beanbag chair. He must have already been learning from Mr. Dunnigan, because he stared at Sam's face and said nothing. Like John Dunnigan, Russ had learned a long time ago to be comfortable with silence. At times more ministering can be done with silence than with words. This was one of those.

"The court clerk called today and they want to see us at 9 A.M. Monday. I expected to be home with my wife and kids tonight. Instead, here I sit watching television and I don't even know what's on. The court clerk told us how routine dropping the restraining order should be, without domestic violence involved, but something has happened."

Sam finished with a comment that brought Russ straight out of the beanbag chair. "Maybe God has failed me."

"No sir. I pray I never hear that phrase roll out of your mouth again," Russ challenged in a voice that was the loudest Sam had ever heard from him. "We may fail our Lord God, but He has never and will never fail even one of His children. He has a plan and a purpose behind all of this. Man, where is your faith? Did you leave it at the bank at five o'clock?"

For the next few minutes you would've thought Russ was preaching, as he stood in the middle of that small living room and gave Sam scripture after scripture from the Bible he was rapidly thumbing through. It seemed that Russ was reminding Sam of most of God's 66,000 promises to His people from the Bible.

Midway through the mini-sermon, Sam sat up, put on his shoes and tied them. He flattened his hair with his hand. You would not have to know much about body language to know that Sam was right then crawling out of his pit and coming into the presence of his God.

The night ended on a good note with the two men praying as usual at the kitchen table. That night the apartment 111 prayers were focused on their wives and Judge Bahnsen, just as it would every night before Monday.

Sunday morning Sam gave Russ some excuses why he could not attend church that day, none of which were acceptable to his roommate. "God is there waiting for you. Are you going to disappoint Him by not showing up? The devil can have the pity party because he's good at that. God needs you today and not the devil. I'm done in the bathroom so you can shower and shave."

At 11:15 A.M. the two were in Sam's car and headed for church together.

When they took their regular seats, Russ saved the seat next to him as usual for his wife. Sam made no effort to save a seat for Becky.

Russ said in a voice loud enough for people being seated around them to hear, "Don't forget to save your wife a seat." Russ was not about to let months of his discipleship and this man's tremendous Christian growth go down the drain without a fight.

Rather than have a dispute with his roommate just before church, Sam reached over and put a bulletin over the seat next to him. Of all the Sundays he had done this, today would be the one day that Becky would not be showing up. She was so fearful of being in contempt of court that she had not even called him all week. He had one email from her and that was the reply regarding Monday's court date.

As the service started and praise music began, Russ was sitting in his usual seat on the aisle. He was in worship and not paying attention to what was going on around them when a woman touched his arm and said, "Excuse me, is that seat taken?" She pointed to the empty seat next to Russ. It was Becky with a big smile on her face. Russ jumped into the aisle and gave her a big bear hug. Out of his side vision, Sam, who was focused on the Lord, was aware that Russ was talking to someone. A second later Sam was stunned when his wife sat down in the empty seat next to him.

Becky nudged up against her husband and whispered, "If I am going to jail for contempt, might as well enjoy it."

That morning, for the first time Sam and Becky worshiped the Lord, really worshiped the Lord, as husband and wife together in church.

There was an usher at Fellowship Church who worked the aisle where the guys always sat. Every week he attempted to give away the two seats being saved for their wives. Russ was just thrilled and praising God to be sitting one empty seat away from Sam's wife who he had been praying for so fervently. As the usher moved slowly down the aisle looking for empty seats, Russ got his attention and motioned for him to bend over to him.

Pointing at Becky he said "Told you she was coming!" It was as much of a "gotcha" moment as a Christian could ever experience. Now Russ had only one seat left to fill.

Satan just does not want us to enjoy those moments, does he? Even in the joy of having his wife next to him for the first time, the evil one attempted to remind Sam of all the professional people who attended church at Fellowship. What if that judge he was about to see happened to be sitting right behind him? What would he do Monday morning?

And yes, Sandy. Sandy the nurse that Sam had mistakenly moved in with for a short time. What if she was in that service and attacked Becky afterward, thinking she had caused Sam to leave the note and to leave that sinful relationship? In quick order, Sam envisioned a fight right in church between the two women. He thought about the police officer who worked the detail for each service having to break up the fight, everybody going to jail, even him for violating the restraining order.

What Sam did next demonstrated how far he had come in his Christian growth. He tore off the corner of a bulletin and wrote, "Pls pray-having thought problems." Sam discreetly folded that very small corner of the page. He put his hand behind his wife's shoulders and got Russ' attention. Russ quietly moved the note to the Bible on his lap, where he opened the note and read it. Russ slowly nodded his head without ever looking at Sam and Becky. Russ' eyes then closed. This guy was not dozing off in church, but rather carrying the immediate needs of his brother before the Lord.

Sam turned his thoughts from the "what ifs" of life, 97% of which will never happen, to the joy and the blessing of having his covenant wife at his side in church, shoulder-to-shoulder and holding hands. In just a minute Sam felt as if he had been given a sedative. In truth, he had been given a sedative, not one created by man, but a sedative from our Lord God.

After church, Sam was unsure if his wife would dart out quickly, or if she would want to talk. After the last amen, Becky walked out of church with her husband proudly at her side. Becky headed for the front of the Bookstore where she had arranged to meet Grant. As they made their way among scores of others in the crowded lobby of the church, Becky reached up and took her husband's hand. Sam squeezed back tightly.

In front of the bookstore stood Grant and Pastor Jim Jackson, the youth pastor who had led Grant to the Lord only a few weeks before. Grant was relaxed and looked happy as he chatted with Pastor Jackson. Was he ever shocked to see his mom walk up, holding hands with his dad.

Introductions were made all around. Pastor Jackson complimented the Sullivans on what a fine son they had.

"We look forward to Grant being part of our youth group for many years."

Pastor Jackson continued, "Grant shared a family secret with me this morning. He asked me to be praying for you tomorrow morning as you go to court. I promise you that I will, and congratulations on the restoration of your marriage. I'm asking God to bless your family and to use your family in His service for a long time."

It is hard to dislike the pastor who led your child to the Lord, but there was something about Pastor Jackson that Sam really liked. He had such a relaxed and understanding way about him.

"I know this isn't the time to go into detail, but I do want to offer my help to you if needed. I am on the staff here at Fellowship as a youth pastor, but my training is in biblical counseling. I do not want to get in the way, but if I can help you in any way with your restoration process, please don't hesitate to call me. Your son even has my cell phone number.

"Many couples forget that marriage restoration is a process and not a one-time event. The absent spouse comes home and everyone gives up praying and standing for that marriage. Soon that husband and wife find themselves in trouble once again. I pray that you two will always stay close to the Lord and close to each other. There's a lot at stake in your beautiful family, as well as in generations to come. May I pray for you before we go?" Pastor Jackson inquired.

Private prayer in the lobby of Fellowship Church was not unusual, but this foursome of husband, wife, son, and youth pastor was unique. Hands have never been held tighter than in that circle. It would not be surprising to hear there was a glow about that group.

Unknown to Sam and Becky, Pastor Jackson had already begun family counseling with the Sullivans. When they had walked up, the pastor was talking with Grant about his dad coming home. He was very carefully talking with Grant about how super it had been that Grant had become the man of the house while his dad was gone. He was telling Grant that once his dad is home, his dad was head of the family. Grant had to step back just a bit.

"Buddy, there will be a day when you meet a girl God has to be your wife for life. That's when you become head of your family, but do not try to take that role away from your dad now. You've already learned a little bit about praying, so you can pray for your parents every day. God hears your prayers."

That day was the start of a family relationship between Pastor Jim Jackson and the Sullivan family that would endure for many decades. Sam and Becky did later go to him for counseling during their restoration. Beyond that, whenever there was a family crisis, Pastor Jackson would always be the first one to be called.

Since Sam was already in violation of his restraining order, he walked Becky and Grant to the car. After opening Becky's door and her getting into the car, Sam leaned in and gave her a kiss. Grant, sitting in the passenger seat next to his mom was beaming. Sam walked around the car opened his son's door and gave him a hug, at the same time saying, "Thanks son, for taking good care of your mom while I've been gone. I'm sorry for everything that happened. Please forgive me and I can promise you that with God's help things are going to be different when I get home. You are my oldest son, our firstborn, and so very special to me. Thanks again for being a little man for your mother."

With that, Sam closed his son's passenger door. It was not until Grant was grown that he would tell his father how much those words, piggybacked on Pastor Jackson's counsel, had meant to him that Sunday.

We really live in an instant society today. The world wants to tell us that quicker is always better. Everything from who provides the fastest DSL service right down to who delivers pizza the fastest, is based on the false concept of quicker being better. That is not always the way our Lord God works. The words that Sam had just imparted to his son seemed not to take fruit until Grant was married, but in truth, those words were like cement being poured into the foundation upon which Grant would build his walk with Christ as well as his life.

Pastor Jackson's talk with Grant and then Sam's words to his oldest are a reminder to you and me to not attempt to use quick drying cement as we build foundations for our families. Neither should we attempt to justify the use of the sand of sin for a foundation and expect our children to build successful lives upon it.

Both Sam and Becky had sleepless Sunday nights, across town from each other. Long before 9 A.M. the following morning, both could be found sitting far from each other on the wooden benches outside room 1404 at the Broward County Courthouse, waiting for the courtroom doors to open. They pretended to not even know each other and took seats on the opposite side of the courtroom, both praying intensely. As court time drew closer, the room began to fill with satchel-carrying attorneys and people. Sam noted how it almost seemed that the men were sitting on one side and the women on the other. Without question, family matters were being heard in the courtroom on that Monday.

At 9 A.M. sharp a loud voice from the court bailiff rang out. "Please stand, court is now in session, the honorable William Bahnsen presiding. You are instructed to remove all hats, mute all cell phones and electronic devices and dispose of chewing gum. You are not to place your feet on the seats. No liquids or foods are allowed in the courtroom."

Sam had appeared in court several times on banking matters, but he had never heard a bill of instructions like these given. It was obvious they had drawn a no-nonsense judge. Becky wished she was next to her husband and had the comfort of his hand to hold.

Neither of the Sullivans had to be fearful for long because their case was called first.

"Sullivan vs Sullivan in the matter of civil drop charge of restraining order," the court clerk rang out.

Sam and Becky arose from opposite sides of the courtroom to go and stand before the judge. They only glanced at each other as if strangers. No one in that room could imagine these two people having spent a weekend together only nine days before.

"I have your petition before me to dismiss a restraining order and I have called you to stand before me at this time. Would both of you please turn and face the gallery?"

Sam and Becky both suspected they were in bad trouble if this judge was going to make an example out of them. He wanted everyone else to see what happens when a restraining order is violated. It was tough for this couple to be only a foot apart at a very emotional time and not be able to even touch their spouse for support. Judge Bahnsen began to speak, only adding to the Sullivans' fear.

"This matter could have been handled in chambers and I requested you here as the first case on a Monday morning to be an example of what can happen. All day today and tomorrow and every day this week, I will be doing what the law requires me to do in the dissolution of marriages. I may be the judge sitting on the bench, but it breaks my heart to send couples out that door in opposite directions, when there isn't any possibility of reconciliation.

"This couple has worked through their problems. They stand here today requesting that a restraining order be dismissed, which I gladly do. Beyond that, I want each of you who are here on a family court matter today, to ask yourselves if you could not give just a bit and work out your problems instead of killing your marriage."

Sam and Becky were both aware of some eye contact between spouses sitting far apart in that courtroom. They witnessed one man get up and move to sit beside the woman who was obviously his wife. Even in Judge Bahnsen's strict courtroom, at that moment such a move was not only acceptable, but it was welcomed.

"I have seen couples leave this courtroom, divorced as one of them wanted, ready to hate for the rest of their lives the person they once loved. The real victims are the children. Divorce is one of the cruelest forms of child abuse. Study after study has shown that if you go through with what you want to do today, your children are disadvantaged for life."

Sam had taken a step toward Becky and now had his arm around her waist.

"If any of you who are in this courtroom right now wish to mutually agree to drop the divorce proceedings, we can do that next.

"Mr. and Mrs. Sullivan, may your marriage be blessed and long. You have started my week on the right note and I suspect your example has given some more people in this room something to think about."

As Judge Bahnsen finished his monologue, he signed a paper with a large flourishing movement of his arm and hand and handed the paper to his clerk. He turned back and nodded at the Sullivans. It was one of those "you may now kiss the bride" moments. Sam took Becky in his arms and gave her a long kiss. As Becky opened her eyes, she saw that hard-nosed judge smiling at them.

Somewhere in the back of the room one person started to applaud, and then some on the other side. There were some attorneys that did not know what to do, but most of the people in that room applauded the couple as they walked out the back door of the courtroom to rebuild their lives together.

Neither Sam nor Becky ever heard what happened in that courtroom for the rest of that day, but I certainly would not have wanted to be the petitioner in the case that followed. Even if every couple went forward with their divorce and left with a divorce decree in their hand, they also left with something implanted in their hearts, that marriage restoration is possible.

Chapter 24

The Homecoming

Sam did not know what to expect at court so he had taken a personal day on Monday. When Sam's faith would weaken, he could easily imagine being jailed for contempt of court. To make matters worse, over the weekend he had heard a news story about a man in Central Florida who, through unusual circumstances, had been jailed because his lawn was brown.

Sam had told Russ, "If they can put that man in jail for what started out as a dead lawn, just imagine what they could do to me for contempt of court. I do not want to have to make my one phone call from jail to the bank to tell them why I will not be in at all on Monday."

As you can probably imagine by now, Russ used the opportunity to teach Sam a bit more about sustaining faith; faith that carries us through no matter how deep the valley or how vicious the storm.

That Monday morning about 9:45 A.M. Sam and Becky Sullivan walked out of the courtroom husband and wife, married for life, with no legal paper telling them what they could not do. Hand in hand, they went down the elevator and started across the walkway to the parking garage. Most everyone going to court must have arrived, because there was very little pedestrian traffic on that walkway. Sam knew what he must do, so midway over S. E. 3rd Avenue, he stopped.

Turning to Becky and looking squarely into her eyes he asked, "Once again, Becky, my wife, I want to ask you to forgive me for being a poor example of a husband. Please forgive me for putting my job first. Please forgive me for not leading our family into becoming a Christian family. My wife, would you allow me to move back home to be the good Christian husband that you deserve?"

"Of course, Sam. We both knew you'd be coming back home once we had the legal issues settled."

"I have taken your love for granted for 14 years, all the time we've been married and I cannot do it any longer. First, I need your forgiveness and then second I need to ask you if you would have me back to try one more time. I can promise you, things will be different with Jesus in our family."

In all of their time together, Sam had never sent Becky a single love letter. He had never been as humble as he was right then, literally standing atop a busy street on a Monday morning outside the county courthouse. Did she ever love this man.

With tears in her eyes, Becky replied, "Sam, you're forgiven for everything you might feel you've done wrong to me in our marriage. I need to also ask you to forgive me in any way that I have failed you as a wife. Yes, my husband, I would welcome you back at home just as soon as you can get there."

Sam and Becky embraced and kissed and then embraced and kissed some more. This was their moment.

An attorney coming into the courthouse walked right past them on that suspended walkway. "You can sure tell who's at the courthouse to get a marriage license," he said to himself after passing them. "They'll cool off real quick."

That attorney was incorrect. What this couple had

discovered, is what a marriage can be like when Jesus is made the focus, instead of individual needs being the focus. It will never "cool off."

The Sullivans left the courthouse parking garage in separate cars. They went to the Sullivan home. Sam was emotional as he pulled that black BMW into the driveway of his own home for the first time in many months. Becky was thrilled to have to watch out for her door not hitting her husband's car when she opened the door.

Even though they had not been at the courthouse for a marriage license, Sam and Becky were behaving like newlyweds. Every few minutes they were together one of them initiated a kiss with the other.

Standing in front of the front door, Becky said, "You unlock it, honey. You live here and are the head of this family."

Sam had long dreamed of this moment. In the past months, he would lie awake at night and recall what their family home looked like. How he missed the chatter of the three precious children that he loved. Sam reached in his pocket and pulled out his keys. He fumbled for a minute to find the door key that had not been used for months.

After unlocking and opening the door, Sam looked at his wife and asked, "Do you remember what I did when we entered this home after it was officially ours? I acted old-fashioned and carried you across the threshold. Would you allow me to do that once again?"

Even though Becky was a bit heavier and Sam was a bit weaker, he picked up his wife and carried her to the door. The first time he did that, years ago, it was out of tradition.

This time it was out of a promise that he would always be Becky's protector. No matter how much it hurt his aging back, this was something Sam had to do.

Once inside the home, holding Becky's hand, he pulled her through every room. His emotions at that moment, of recovering what he thought was lost forever, were beyond description. Becky was also touched by the moment, but more so by the three words Sam kept repeating all through his tour; "Thank You, Jesus...Thank You, Jesus...Thank You, Jesus." On that day, and every day since, Sam and Becky gave credit for their marriage being restored to Jesus Christ alone.

Sam's belongings were still in the apartment off of McNab Road in Pompano. His invitation to Becky to go with him to collect his personal effects thrilled her. She had only imagined what the apartment looked like where Sam and Russ lived. On the way to the apartment, riding in Sam's car, she wished there were no seatbelts. Becky wanted to be right next to her hubby.

As Sam pulled into the apartment complex, he pointed out some landmarks to his wife. He showed her Russ' car. He especially wanted her to see the tree that he and Russ had sat under on the Saturday afternoon when he had repented of his sins and had given his heart and life to Jesus.

On the way out to the apartment Sam had called Russ, who knew they were coming. Russ had also heard of the events in court that morning. As the Sullivans approached apartment 111 the door seemed to open by itself.

Good natured and godly Russ came out to greet them. After rejoicing over what happened that morning and over the fact that Russ was losing a roommate because he was going home to his wife, the trio started for the opened door.

"I'm sorry but you can't come in," Russ said to Becky with a serious look on his face. "My roommate and I have an agreement that we would never allow any woman into our apartment."

Although the statement was true, Becky did not know that Russ was only joking about her going inside. That little woman could hold her own with Russ. "So, when your wife comes back to you, you're going to tell her she's not allowed inside?" Even though they were joking about Becky not coming inside, she was greatly impressed by just another indication of the godly lives her husband and Russ had been living.

"Well, I'll have to check with my roommate. Maybe we can make an exception for our own wives, but only on the day we are moving home to them."

As Becky entered apartment 111 she was amazed at how plain it was. In the living room was an old sofa with worn fabric, a beat up coffee table, one end table and a beanbag chair. Even though the apartment was clean and appeared well-maintained, little white balls had been leaking out of the beanbag onto the floor. Around the corner of the small apartment, Becky could see the kitchen table that her husband had described to her so well. There was a small framed photo of a woman who must have been Russ' wife. A second framed photo lay face down on the table. There were also two Bibles and several neat stacks of paperwork on the table.

Walking into the kitchen, Becky's curiosity caused her to do something that was out of place for her. She opened the door to the guys' refrigerator. It was almost empty, but it was cleaner than her own refrigerator at home. On the top shelf were doggie bag type containers from several inexpensive restaurants. Over on the door was quite a collection of mustard and ketchup packets. Just about any topping you could want was represented there. They were fortunate to have them because there were no bottled condiments in the refrigerator.

Becky was ashamed when she realized the tight budget her husband had been living under. She and the kids had been enjoying their home while Sam lived in a cracker box with some old furnishings. She did not know how, but right then she started asking God to give her a way to make up to her husband for what she had caused by signing the restraining order.

The apartment was a cracker box and the furnishings obsolete, but it was evident that this was a house of prayer. Christian posters decorated many of the walls and Christian music was playing from a secondhand CD player sitting on the floor in the hallway.

Becky and Sam walked into his bedroom to get his belongings. Deep inside, it might have been a suspicious spirit, but Becky was checking that bedroom really well. There were not even any secular magazines in there, no television, nothing we would say is of the world. Sam still had the cardboard boxes from a week ago Sunday and he began to gather up his belongings to move home.

Becky was impressed that Sam's clothing was all neatly hung, with the hangers facing in one direction, just as Sam had at home. Her husband had been sleeping on a bed that was far too small for him. Once again Becky silently asked God to give her a way, a special way, to make up to her husband for her causing all of this.

This apartment was 180 degrees from what you might expect a man to be living in. There was an atmosphere of peace, a godly atmosphere throughout all of apartment 111.

Russ helped with the packing and loading of Sam's car. When everything was done and it was time to leave, Russ picked up a photo of his wife from the table and handed it to Becky.

"Could I ask you to take this as a prayer reminder for my wife? It's the only photo I have of her, but I will never forget what she looks like. Please, would you take it and pray for us?" Russ pleaded.

Becky caught her husband between trips to the car and asked what she should do. Together they had a plan, something they wanted to do anyway. They would accept the photo for now, invite Russ to dinner and have a copy of the photo made for him before he arrived.

Back inside, Sam wrote Russ a check for his share of the rent and expenses for three months.

"Brother, you shouldn't do this. There's no obligation, because I am the one who signed the lease," Russ humbly responded.

"Brother, Becky and I talked about this on the way out here this morning. It is something we want to do. I'm basically leaving you without notice," Sam retorted.

Russ got one of those goofy Russ grins on his face and said, "No notice? I had several months notice. When you told me you were praying for marriage restoration, I had my notice that you were leaving. Man, haven't I taught you anything about faith?"

Becky joined the conversation about the check. "Please

accept this from both of us. I have already learned that you cannot outgive God. If you don't accept it, Sam said you would be keeping us from receiving a blessing. I've heard a lot about how you minister to other men and this is something that God told my husband to do."

While his wife was talking, Sam was writing the check. He must have miscalculated his half of the rent and expenses for three months, because the check was for $500 too much. Russ was in need until his job started and this was only a token amount to thank him for all that he had done for his brother Sam, starting on that Saturday afternoon when Sam was somehow drawn back into the parking lot to look for Russ' car.

Sam's life, his wife's life, his oldest son's life, his marriage, and soon the lives of his two younger children would be forever changed, and I do mean forever, not only on this earth and in this life, but in life eternal with Jesus where they will each be someday.

Sam and Becky invited Russ to dinner on Thursday night. It had to be Thursday, because Wednesday was church night and Friday night Sam had something very special that he had to do. This couple was looking forward to having Russ meet their children as much as Russ was looking forward to meeting the kids that he had been praying for.

As Sam drove out of the parking lot, Russ was standing outside waiting. In a way, Sam felt guilty to be leaving but nothing could ever keep him away from his family.

Sam and Becky had not been at a restaurant alone in many months. He asked his wife where she would like to go for lunch. Sam was thinking of all the nice places where they had enjoyed meals along Las Olas Boulevard. He thought his wife might pick one of the places with an ocean view.

Becky's answer surprised Sam, yet when he thought about it, it didn't really surprise him at all. "Since we are this far up, can we go to Cracker Barrel?"

Cracker Barrel, in nearby Deerfield Beach, had always been a favorite of their kids. To Becky, this represented not just a lunch with her husband, but a family reunited. Sam headed for Cracker Barrel.

The Sullivans barely arrived back at home in time to park Sam's car, leaving it loaded, and get in Becky's car to go pick up their kids from school. All three children knew dad was close to coming home, but they were surprised that he was in the car when they were picked up from school. The hugs between Sam and Becky earlier that day on that pedestrian overpass out of the courthouse were nothing compared to the hugs and kisses exchanged in that car in the next five minutes.

With mom and dad in the front seat and three kids, complete with backpacks, in the rear seat, the intact Sullivan family was in one car together for the first time in a long time. Listening to the excited chatter from his kids, Sam silently reaffirmed right then and there that, with God's help, nothing like the mess they had gone through would ever happen again. Beyond that he promised God that he would raise his kids to become Christian spouses.

Following after school snacks at home, Becky said to her kids, "I think daddy could use some help unpacking his car."

If you ever want to see a motivated child, it would be when they are helping to bring an absent parent's belongings back in the house once and for all. Trousers lying in the front yard, cardboard boxes that were dropped and everything being placed into a big pile in the middle of the living room did not even matter to either parent. What mattered was that daddy was home.

Becky had intended to offer her husband his choice of a special meal for dinner. She asked what really sounded good to him for his first meal back with his family. Would you guess that Sam said Skyline Chili? Sam wasn't that hungry for Skyline, but he knew it was special to the kids. Beyond that, he wanted Tony, the cook at Skyline who had given Becky the card from their bulletin board about a marriage being restored, to see that God had moved in his priceless family.

Just about everything Sam owned was still in that pile in the middle of the living room floor when the family loaded up to go to Skyline for dinner. It was Sam, not Ryan, who suggested they sit at the counter that night.

As you can imagine, Tony was thrilled that Sam was home. He was not nearly as thrilled, though, as a wife and three children were.

"I knew it. I just knew it when I handed you that card that Sam would be back," Tony exclaimed.

"By the way, Tony," Becky interjected, "here is that card back for you to put up on the bulletin board again for the person who needs it next. In a few days I will be sending a second one to put next to it."

That night Sam had the honor of doing homework with his three children. The big mound in the living room was not getting any smaller, but no one seemed to really care. Sam tucked in each of his kids and for the first time in their lives, their daddy prayed with them at bedtime.

Sam was concerned that Connie, their 10-year-old daughter who had made that 911 call, was still carrying a lot of guilt over all that had happened. Of all the things that Sam knew he had to work at correcting, his daughter was high on the list.

As he tucked Connie into bed Sam asked, "Do you know what a date is?"

"Sure daddy, everyone knows what a date is. It's when you get all dressed up and go somewhere with someone you really like. Dates are really special. Daddy, how old do you have to be to go on a date?"

"I think just about your age. Would you like to get all dressed up and go on a date with your daddy on Friday night?" Sam asked the little girl lying in bed. "You can pick whatever restaurant you want that night. It will be a special night for me and my daughter."

Connie's eyes sparkled at the thought of going on a date with her daddy. "I know where I want to go. My friend Kayla from school went on a date with her daddy and they went to a place called, "Melting Pot," where you cook your own food. Can we go there, daddy, please?"

"It's a date," Sam confirmed. "Your mom said she will help you get ready, and I'll pick you up at 6 P.M."

As Sam said goodnight, turned out Connie's light and headed out of her bedroom, Sam heard his daughter call him back.

"Daddy, thank you for coming home, because we really need you."

Sam went out to the living room, where his wife was recovering a suit, shirt and tie to press for Sam to wear to work the next day. As she had done for years, Becky would make it her responsibility to help her banker husband look sharp when he walked out the door.

All five members of the Sullivan family slept better that night than any of them had slept for months.

Sam Sullivan, successful banker turned repo man and now a banker once again, had come home. Above that, he was asked to leave his home a sin-filled man. His family had just received back a Christian man ready to lead his family.

Praise God for the many miracles He works for each of us every day. May you and I never forget Who gives them all to us.

Chapter 25

Back At Home

By Tuesday morning, everything seemed pretty well back to normal around the Sullivan's home, that is if you overlook the mountain still waiting in the center of the living room. There were a couple additions, though. Sam, who used to stay in bed until Becky left to take the kids to school was up at 6:30 A.M. Just as Russ had taught him to do, Sam began his day with private devotions. Be it ever so brief, for now, Sam prayed for his kids and their day before Becky took them out of the house.

As soon as they were on the way to school, Sam dug through the mountain growing in the middle of the living room until he found one of his praise CDs. It sounded so much nicer playing in his own home, especially in place of the secular talk show he would have previously had on in the morning. As Sam showered, with praise music playing in the background, he stood before the bathroom mirror and prayed for his day and for his wife. It was so good to be doing this in his own home. Sam wept as he thanked God for the blessing of being back in his own home.

Sam was a few minutes late to work that day, but no one really minded. When Becky returned from the short drive to take the kids to school and walked in the door of their home, the sound of that praise music was overwhelming to her spirit. She found her husband staring into the mirror and praying. It was one of those special moments, very special, that anyone with a restored marriage can testify to having experienced.

When Sam came home that evening, the mountain in his living room had disappeared. Becky had taken things to the cleaners, hung up other clothing items and had several piles neatly stacked on their bed waiting for Sam to decide where they should be put away. Sam looked to that freshly vacuumed carpet where the mountain had been when he left for work and realized all of what he had gone through was behind him. He had been forgiven by his God many weeks before and he had also been forgiven by his wife.

That evening, when Sam thanked his wife for moving the mountain, not only in their living room, but also in their marriage, Becky told her husband how much it meant to her that he could bring home everything from the apartment, put it in a pile, and allow any of their family to rummage through it, without fear of what they might find. Becky referred to it as "total trust building transparency."

The one-time event of reconciliation had occurred and now the process of restoration was underway, being built upon the mutual trust of two covenant spouses. God was ready to bless this family beyond measure.

Thursday evening, half an hour before Russ was to arrive for dinner with the Sullivans, he called that he was running late. He and Mr. Dunnigan were in a meeting related to setting up the new business. Russ said he would be there within an hour.

When Russ arrived he was not driving the old, well waxed, low fueled car that had seen the back of a repo truck more than once. He was in a brand new Ford Mustang. Russ got out of the car wearing a sharp looking suit. The man really looked great. He could have been mistaken for a banker or attorney.

Sam walked outside to meet him. "Hey buddy, nice car." Sam suspected Russ had somehow been approved for credit and had bought himself a new car, just because he had started a new job.

"It's a company car," Russ explained, grinning as usual. "Mr. Dunnigan wrote a car into my contract with them. He said he could not risk me getting my car repossessed and not coming to work. I can never tell when that man is trying to make a joke and when he is serious."

"Many of us have the same problem. Come on in and meet my kids. They are excited about you coming to have dinner with us since they've been hearing about you from Becky and me. I guess they just wonder what kind of guy would want to be their dad's roommate," Sam invited.

The evening was a total success, to the extent of Ryan wrestling on the floor with his new "Uncle Russ." Becky's meal was great and everyone was relaxed around the table. The kids were on their best behavior.

After dinner, still sitting around the table, Becky got up to go make coffee and shoo the kids into their rooms to do homework. Russ gave Sam an update on the new company. He was already on the payroll and the hosting service was to be housed right in Sam's bank building, which Mr. Dunnigan owned. Russ was excited about the task ahead of him of setting up a web hosting company with all Christian content.

Apart from reports back to Mr. Dunnigan, Russ was pretty much on his own to build the company. He had a free hand to order the equipment he needed and to hire the staff he needed. Best of all, he had the resources of Dunnigan Enterprises' marketing department to help them make the business successful. Russ was living the dream that every IT guy had ever dreamed. Sam knew, as did Mr. Dunnigan, that Russ would never abuse what he had been placed over.

Russ might have had a little trouble finding the Sullivan's address that night, but in the days ahead, "Uncle Russ" would be there so often that he could find their home blindfolded.

Sam's Friday night date with Connie was quite a success also. Apparently, all the kids in her class knew that she was going on a date with her daddy to a fancy restaurant. Friday night that ten-year-old girl looked beautiful and was she ever excited about her date. Sam had stopped on the way home from work and purchased her a rose, which thrilled her. Daddy opened the car door for his date and did everything he could to make her feel special.

That night, driving out to Coral Springs, Sam realized as he listened to his daughter tell one story after another, that before that evening he had never really listened to his daughter one-on-one. What a shame it would have been for that precious girl to have grown up and to leave home without really knowing her dad, one-on-one.

That night at the Melting Pot restaurant, father and daughter had quite an evening. Connie even brought up the 911 call she had made. This entire night was worth the 60 seconds they spent forgiving one another over that call.

Even at age 10, Connie demonstrated so many of her mother's nurturing traits as she attempted to make sure everything at the table was just right for the date. On the way home, Connie asked Sam, "How long do we have to wait before we go on another date, daddy?"

"Not long, honey, not long at all." As he drove Connie talked, but Sam made a renewed commitment to his Lord to never again overlook his precious daughter.

The following Sunday Sam proudly took his entire family

to church. On the way, with all the happy chatter in the car, Sam thought about that Sunday that seemed so long ago, when he left his hotel and went in search of the church, any church, that would ease his pain. He discovered a church, but it failed him very badly.

That Sunday morning on the way to church, Sam promised the Lord that as long as he lived, regardless of what church he might be in, that he would do his part to help that church meet the needs of hurting people who God sent to them.

Sam Sullivan seemed to have been making Jesus one promise after another, but that is normal for a person who's had their eyes opened to the guilt of a family that God has given them, and they have been overlooking for so long.

After a marriage is restored, there are good events, but some nevertheless break the heart of a husband and wife. This family experienced one when Ryan was named student of the month at his school. It would have been different a year before, but this time Sam knew enough about his role as a father, to leave his job in the middle of a workday and drive to Ryan's school to see him surprised by his award. After the small ceremony had ended, Ryan's teacher was talking with her student and his parents, congratulating him on the good behavior and good grades that earned him that award.

Ryan made a comment that every parent absent from their family by their own choice should be made to hear.

"I got it because my daddy came home and everything is back like it was, Miss Madison. I am sorry I was so bad in school when my daddy was gone, but that is the only way anybody would pay attention to me." The restoration process was at work in every member of this family.

A few weeks later, on a Sunday afternoon, the Sullivan family drove to the beach in Pompano where Becky and her son Grant were baptized together, just as Sam had been. The two younger kids stood on the beach with a daddy giving praise to God for an event he never thought he would see. As you can imagine, the Dunnigans and the Tomlinsons were also present.

As Becky was raised from the water to walk "...in newness of life," the first sounds she heard were applause and amens from people she loved and cared about deeply.

Connie and Ryan were curious about baptism and what it meant. That night their mom and dad sat down with them to answer their questions. It amazed Sam that they had learned so much in such a short time attending Sunday school and church. It amazed Sam even more when Connie said, "I think it is time for me to ask Jesus into my heart."

During his long life and career Sam Sullivan would lead scores of people to the Lord, but none touched him more than the first two converts he won for Christ. He carefully explained the great gift that God has given us to his son and daughter, being careful that they comprehended what they were doing. Sam then prayed with them to receive Jesus Christ.

Sam Sullivan had quite a Sunday. Foremost he was right with the Lord, second he was home with his family and in a right relationship with them. Sam had four family members under his roof. On that day he witnessed two of them being baptized and the other two coming to Christ.

That night, standing in the shower, where Sam seemed to do serious thinking, he imagined where he and his family might be right now, had he and Becky not reconciled, allowing Jesus to handle their differences.

You might be wondering if everything was perfect for Sam and Becky. No marriage is perfect, but here's the difference; do you handle the problems yourselves or do you allow Jesus to handle them? That really is the "before and after" of a restored marriage.

There were even some heated exchanges in which things were uttered in anger like "I never should have come back" and even, "The attorney was right." A few times satan even dropped "You'll never change" into their dialogue. Every time this couple would have those "moments of intense fellowship," as every couple experiences once in a while, the encounters ended not with the argument being escalated, nor with a child so frightened she called 911. Instead the couple called on the name of Jesus.

Any strife or potential strife vanishes once it is placed at the foot of the cross. How is this done? The key might be forgiveness, with each spouse caring more about their mate than themselves. Regardless of what happens between Sam and Becky, regardless of what happens between your storyteller and his wife, regardless of what happens between you and your spouse, if it is recognized as strife coming from satan and is given to Jesus, it vanishes.

Trust me. I've been there and done that. Praise Jesus for touching and protecting couples.

After becoming a Christian and while he was away from home, Sam had become convicted about the air of his driving a sleek BMW. The other brothers in the Bible study, starting with Russ, had hardly been able to keep a car running, while Sam received notices on scheduled oil changes at the import car dealers.

One night, back at the apartment and alone in his room, just before falling asleep Sam promised God that if He would heal his marriage, Sam would exchange his leased BMW for something less affluent.

Becky was totally happy with her Ford minivan. In fact, when she and Sam were going out, Becky would often ask if they could take her car instead of the BMW. Sam had leased it basically without his wife's knowledge and he had even sensed that from time to time she was embarrassed to be seen driving a fancy imported car. He knew that both Becky and God would be honored to see that BMW disappear.

One afternoon on the way home from the bank, Sam had called home and told Becky he would be delayed about an hour. Sam stopped by the leasing company who owned his car. He discovered how anxious they were to let him out of the BMW agreement if he wanted to sign another lease.

Since Sam had never really consulted with his wife when leasing the BMW, he felt free to go ahead and get out of the car that Becky had never liked. Sam selected a new sand-stone colored Ford Expedition.

Sam was more than an hour late getting home that night. Can you imagine a banker signing a car lease before he had read every line? You know why Sam was late reaching the dinner table at home that evening.

The following Saturday Sam took his boys out to breakfast and then by the leasing company "just to look at cars." Of all the vehicles there, can you imagine which one those two boys loved? Yes, it was the Expedition.

"Let's just take my things out of the old car, put them in the new car and drive it home," Sam said.

“Dad! We can’t do that,” one of them shouted.

“Yes we can. It's my car now. Let’s get my things moved over.”

Back at home, Becky was both shocked and pleased by what her husband had done. She sensed that the ritzy BMW reminded her husband of either life before Christ or of life away from home. Either way, she was thrilled that black BMW was gone.

Everyone feels that our children are resilient to divorce, when in fact it’s tearing them up. Ryan just loved that car, but that afternoon while they were playing in it he told his brother, “Daddy just got it so he’ll have more room for stuff when he leaves us again.” It would take time and relationship building, but someday he would laugh about ever having made that comment.

There was another comment made on that Saturday that Becky never questioned aloud what it meant. When Sam drove up in the new Expedition one of the first things he said was, “Missionaries don’t drive BMWs.”

Becky wondered if Sam intended to give more to the church's mission program or did he mean something else? Her immediate vision was of that vehicle parked outside a mud hut somewhere. Was her husband talking about helping a missionary or being a missionary? Even though a very young Christian, Becky knew that God was in control, regardless of what message Sam had unknowingly dictated to a Dragon.

Chapter 26

The Rest Of The Story

During the following weeks, the Sullivan family continued on their path toward total marriage restoration. Each of the five were adjusting to once again being a family; only now, this family was serving Jesus.

It seemed like everything that happened to Sam Sullivan happened on Monday, the worst day of the week for a banker. Several weeks after his return home, Sam's cell phone rang mid-afternoon on Monday. He saw Becky's cell phone number as the incoming call. Becky knew what Mondays were like for her husband. She seldom called him at work at all, especially on a Monday. Sam was afraid that Becky had car trouble or that one of the kids was sick.

"Hi, honey," Sam answered. "Is everything all right?" He always liked the informality of Becky calling him on the cell phone instead of her going through the bank's telephone system and the secretary to reach "Mr. Sullivan's office."

"Everything is great, but I did have a question." As soon as Sam heard the first couple of words from his wife, he knew that nothing was wrong.

"What is your question, my dear wife?"

"I was thinking about the weekend in South Georgia when we met each other kind of by accident, except that it had been arranged. Did you bring anything home to remind us of that weekend, something like a rock?"

'No, I didn't. That weekend was a milestone in our

marriage. You and I have never talked together so much since we've been married. It was great. Now that you mention it, I should've brought home that Fort Pierce sign I made for you, since that cottage reminded both of us of Fort Pierce where I-95 and the Florida Turnpike, once going different directions, come back together."

"Sam, I just discovered that I brought something back from that weekend I think you'll like. In fact I think you will love it." Becky had a habit of doing deep housecleaning while the kids were at school so Sam suspected his wife had come across a napkin from that restaurant or her receipt for the coconut doughnuts. Other than that, he could not imagine what Becky had discovered she brought back from that weekend.

As Sam often did when talking on a cell phone, he was pacing in his office. It somehow relieved the stress of sitting at a desk all day. "Honey, are you pacing?" Becky asked. "If you are, please sit down because I don't want you passing out and getting blood on the bank's carpet in the event you hit your head. Tell me that you're sitting down, and I'll tell you what I brought back for us."

Sam laughed at how well his wife knew him. He suspected Becky could tell by his voice whether he was sitting or pacing. Before he answered he sat down in his chair, "Okay, honey," Sam announced. He could hardly wait to hear what foolishness she had discovered.

"Honey, I brought back something from that weekend for us that I didn't even know was there. Sam, we're pregnant."

Times like this might be where the phrase "pregnant pause" originated. Sam Sullivan, once again, was speechless.

"I just walked out of the doctor's office, and he confirmed the pregnancy. I have not been feeling just right and I wondered if..., but surely not. I mean, after all..." Sam was not the only one having trouble finding the right words for the moment.

As soon as the stun of the pregnancy news wore off, Sam and Becky rejoiced. They were bringing another child into the world that would not be here if they had not reconciled.

"Are we having a boy or a girl?" Sam excitedly asked.

"Honey, I just found out. It's too soon!"

The Sullivan kids did not know why their dad was home from work about an hour early on Monday. Sam just wanted to be with his wife, so he had left work. He did have a stop to make for the bank on the way, so under these circumstances, that justified leaving early.

Three kids could not imagine what their parents were having a big family meeting about that night. Ryan, the youngest of the bunch, told his brother he was certain that dad was going to say he was leaving again, this time in his big car that the boys enjoyed so much.

That night the kids heard they were going to have a new brother or sister. Connie was the most excited that she was going to be a big sister. Grant pretty well took the news in stride, but Ryan was a kid who was really excited. He said he was excited because he would not be the youngest any longer. It is more likely he was excited that his dad had not said he was leaving again.

In the months ahead, the entire Sullivan home was moved to prepare for the new arrival. A nursery was prepared and painted. It had been seven years since Sam and Becky had a baby, so everything was like starting all over. That home had five excited people. That home also had five people who were praying for the new baby.

Once it was discovered they were having a boy, selection of a name began. There were so many people who had played a role in keeping this family together, it was going to be difficult to select a name. Finally Sam and Becky decided that he would select the first name and she would select the middle name for their unborn son.

"None of the rest would have been possible had a man out waxing an old car not taken time to tell me about Jesus. I would like for our son's first name to be Russell," Sam decided rather quickly. When Sam added, "We could call him Rusty," he had no idea that his unborn son, being formed and developed in his wife's womb would have rust colored hair, much like Sam's own.

Like any woman making such a decision, Becky took much longer in deciding on a middle name. She looked for a biblical name that would describe the circumstances she and Sam had endured with the help of Jesus, but nothing really seemed to fit. She considered the name of her father and of Sam's father, but nothing really struck her.

One night during her pregnancy when she was uncomfortable and could not sleep, with her husband holding her hand, she asked Sam a question.

"Do you remember that Ft. Pierce sign you made for me and stuck on the cottage? Sam, that meant so much to me after hearing your illustration about how the two roads paralleled and then separated, but came back together at Ft. Pierce. How crazy would you think I am if I wanted Pierce to be our son's middle name?"

"Becky, I love it. I absolutely love it! Would that be because of where Rusty was conceived or because of where our roads came back together?" Sam asked.

"Everything about the Fort Pierce illustration, the cabin, how we went there separately, just everything. Where the name came from could be a little family secret. You can say you wanted a name that sounded like a banker and Russell Pierce Sullivan sounds like a banker, doesn't it?" Becky said.

She continued, "Do you remember the day that you moved home, when you took me to your apartment and you were packing? I saw how you had been living, the empty refrigerator, the undersized bed, practically no furniture and all the rest. That day, standing in your apartment watching you get your things together to come home, I asked God to please give me a way, a special way, that I could do something for you to make up for what I caused to happen. Sam, God is allowing me to give birth to Rusty for you. Of all our children, he will always be special."

Becky's tender comments were enough to earn her one of those back rubs from Sam that mothers-to-be seem to crave. Very shortly, Sam and Becky were again fast asleep, anxiously awaiting the birth of their child.

The following week Sam's secretary called on the intercom that he had an emergency call from his wife. He picked up the phone instantly to hear a sobbing Becky.

"Sam, I don't know what to do! Please help me!" Becky screamed hysterically .

"Calm down, honey, calm down so I can know what's

wrong so I can help you."

"There's something wrong, really wrong with Rusty. It is really bad. The doctor gave me a lot of papers, but I am shaking so bad I can't even read. I can't even drive. Sam, they say if I don't have an abortion soon the problems could kill me! Oh, Sam, what do I do?"

Sam's foremost thought was to help his wife, but at the same time he was furious that someone wanted to kill his son. Sam was grabbing his jacket and briefcase as he talked. "Becky, tell me where you are and I will be right there. I want you to just sit in your car. Start it up to keep you cool and, honey, just relax. The Lord is going to get us through this. Above all else, do not dare go back inside that doctor's office. Now tell me where you are, I'm on the way."

The same doctor that had delivered the Sullivan's first three children had been caring for Becky during this pregnancy, and Sam was on the way double time to his office where his sobbing wife sat in her car in the parking lot. Sam was literally running as he passed his secretary and shouted "family emergency."

Sam manipulated the Expedition with one hand while calling Fellowship Church with the other. He and Becky had counseled with Pastor Jim Jackson. Sam's hysterical voice to the Church receptionist was enough to get him put right through to Pastor Jim. Prayer was needed for his unborn son right now, as there was a problem and the doctor wanted to do an abortion.

Pastor Jim asked where Becky was right then. Sam told him the name of the doctor and that he was on the way. Pastor Jim promised to get prayer warriors notified within minutes. Actually, it was going to be Pastor Jim's secretary who sent out the urgent prayer request. Pastor Jim was on his way out the door, on the double, to go minister to this couple in their time of crisis.

It is a wonder that Sam did not get a ticket as he carefully ran red lights, drove over the edge of sidewalks to get around stopped traffic, and had the horn blowing almost all the way to the Sunrise Boulevard doctor's office. At one point Sam thought, "If a cop stops me, I'll just tell him it's a matter of life or death, because it's the life or death of my son." That's when he drove up the median for about half a block to get around traffic.

Sam came flying into the doctor's parking lot and stopped behind Becky's car. He jumped out and flew to his wife's side.

Even in her hysteria, while waiting for Sam to arrive, Becky had called Susan Tomlinson and asked her to pick up the kids and watch them. Becky was sobbing greatly and told Susan the doctor wanted to abort Rusty. Susan knew that her husband's agency insured many local physicians. She asked Doug who he knew that was good and could he pull strings to get Becky in right away if needed.

Doug Tomlinson instantly knew who to call and ask for a great favor. His agency insured Dr. Harvey Knutson. The doctor had such an excellent reputation in the community that his practice was closed to new patients. He was active in local pro-life activities and was on the cutting edge of the latest medical advances in the area of women's health.

In addition to being Dr. Knutson's insurance agent, the Tomlinsons also knew them socially. Doug placed a call and within a minute had the doctor on the phone. Doug explained what he knew about the situation and that abortion was suggested for the next morning.

To have a friend call and say their best friend is being counseled to abort lit Harvey Knutson's fire. If they wanted to see him, send the expectant mother right over and she would be worked in as a patient without delay.

Let's take stock of where we are. About 28 minutes ago a doctor suggested Becky have an abortion. At this moment people all over the world are praying after Fellowship Church sent out an urgent email prayer request. The mother-to-be is sitting in her car outside that doctor's office. Her husband is driving over sidewalks to get to her side. From another direction, their pastoral counselor is coming almost as fast. Their next-door neighbor is picking up the children from school and the best woman's doctor in Fort Lauderdale is waiting to see her. God does take care of his people. He is not about to have Rusty killed by abortion.

Susan had told her husband Doug where Becky was. The doctor 's office was not far from his insurance agency, so he left the office and headed there taking Harvey Knutson's private cell phone number with him.

No one took time to pull into a parking place as a husband, a pastor and an insurance agent arrived in rapid succession. They seemed to be having their own pro-life rally in that parking lot.

All three men looked at the paperwork that the doctor had given Becky. Doug told of his call to Dr. Knutson. Becky and Sam wanted to go see him right away. Pastor Jim remembered to ask about Becky's medical records as they sat in the parking lot. Doug explained to Sam and Becky about the release of medical records and how her signature would be needed.

"I do not want her back in the office of anyone who suggested killing our unborn son," Sam announced emphatically.

Becky was comfortable in her car with the air-conditioner on, so it was decided that Pastor Jim would stay with her while Sam and Doug went inside to get a release for the records. They would bring it out to Becky for her signature and then go inside and wait for the records.

As you might expect, they met opposition at the front desk. Doug asked to see the office manager. He was polite but firm as he explained the predicament that office was in, dropping a bomb shell on a patient as they had just done.

Doug just happened to mention that he was an insurance agent and knew just a bit about malpractice. "The prudent thing for your doctor to do would be to release this woman's records so that she can go to the physician she chooses for a second opinion before anyone aborts her unborn child. Malpractice cases often start as things like this."

Yes, Doug was polite, but by the end, he had increased in volume just enough to be heard all over the waiting room, causing half a dozen very pregnant women to look up at the window to see what was happening.

Suddenly Sam's signature was going to be sufficient for the release of records since he was the husband and was listed on the chart. As Sam was filling out the request for records, Becky's chart was already being copied. Three minutes after the guys went through the door, they were back out with copies of the records.

Pastor Jim did not want to be seen sitting in a car with a woman who was not his wife. He wisely sat in the back seat of the van and left the side door opened with a foot outside on the ground. Pastor Jim had prayer with Becky; did he ever have prayer. Everyone knew there was a life at stake here. After he prayed, Pastor Jim called his secretary from his cell phone. He put on the external speaker and allowed Becky to hear how many prayer requests had gone out by email.

He also asked his secretary to read some of the replies for Becky. Becky looked at ease for the first time as Pastor Jim's secretary read email replies from around the world. A few replies told of their own experiences when they had been told that abortion was necessary but was not done.

The email reply that touched Becky the most was from a young seminary student in South Africa. His mother had been told her son's birth defects were so bad he should be aborted. She did not but instead turned to Jesus for His healing touch and today a young man is a seminary student, preparing to be a pastor. He wrote that he was praying for Becky and for her unborn son and that God had a plan and a purpose for that child; thus satan wanted to destroy him even before birth.

When Becky heard that message read to her, coming from South Africa by email and being read to her over the speaker on the cell phone, Becky heard from God right then that she was to say no to abortion, regardless.

Sam and Doug quickly came out of the office, Becky's medical records in hand. Sam pulled his double parked car into a parking place and jumped behind the wheel of Becky's van. Doug did the same and jumped in the back seat, as did Pastor Jim. While en route, Doug called the new doctor's office to get the exact address and to tell them they were on the way.

Heading west on Broward Boulevard, it was evident that

Pastor Jim was praying fervently. He was taking seriously the position God placed him in at that moment.

Doug disconnected his call from Dr. Knutson. "They're expecting you, Becky. You're going to be in good hands now. Hope I'm not getting in your way, but I wanted to be with you in case you get hung up getting in to see Harvey."

Becky would tell you today that she felt like she was surrounded by angels. Even though she had heard terrible news within the past hour, she now had her husband with her, a pastor with her, and their neighbor/insurance agent who was on a first name basis with the best woman's health doctor. Becky will also tell you about the great peace she experienced, as the presence of the Holy Spirit became very real to her.

Becky was taken right into an exam room while Sam completed her paperwork in the waiting room. As soon as he was done, Sam was taken right in to be with his wife. Another sonogram was immediately done. When Dr. Knutson came into the exam room to introduce himself, he had Becky's medical records from the previous doctor in his hand. Various page corners had been turned down, so obviously he had read through her chart.

After introducing himself, Dr. Knutson looked at Becky's recent sonogram. It would be more accurate to say that he stared at the sonogram for several seconds before he spoke.

"Before we talk about anything I would really like to do another sonogram. We have a higher level machine we use for high-risk patients. That might confirm things for us. I will tell you, regardless of what we do or do not see, you will not hear abortion suggested by me."

Sam sat by his wife's side during the enhanced sonogram. How he wished he could understand what he saw on the screen. He did know enough to understand that was his son, and that he could clearly see heartbeats. After the sonogram was finished, the technician rolled the machine out of the room. For the next few minutes the medical assistant checked on Becky constantly, offering her warm blankets or pillows. Becky thought either she was receiving VIP treatment because of Doug or else this was about the best physician's office she had ever seen.

Pastor Jim and Doug sat in the waiting room, two Christian men, not wasting time on magazines during this time of crisis, but praying for Becky and for her unborn son. Two or three times during the wait, Pastor Jim made discreet calls to the church office. He did not check in for messages, but gave updates on Becky's condition. He inquired about email relevant to the prayer request and at one point asked his secretary to please resend the request with an update. Pastor Jim did not know that he would soon be sending out an answered praise email of praise on Becky's behalf.

As an aside, during the time the two men were waiting, Doug decided he would ask his wife Susan to visit Fellowship Church with him. He had seen such spiritual growth in his neighbors, and now to have a praying pastor sitting next to him topped it off. Some pastors would have used the captive audience of a prominent business owner to politic for their church. Instead, this man stayed in prayer or else made calls related only to this crisis. He was certainly a man called by God and sent for this hour.

When Dr. Knutson re-entered the exam room, he said what every patient fears hearing:

"Well..."

Sam said it was as if the man did not know what to say next. After another pregnant pause, he began to speak.

"I've carefully studied both sonograms that were done in this office this afternoon. Well, let me back up and start another way. I have looked at the sonogram you had done elsewhere earlier this afternoon, and I can see exactly what that doctor saw. In fact, I just talked with him to verify a few things. He and I agree that when you walked out of his office, you and your unborn child were in serious trouble. Now he and I would differ on how we would handle that trouble, but there was total agreement that there was trouble.

"When the first sonogram was done in my office, I did not see what he had seen. That's why I ordered the advanced level sonogram. As of right now I can tell you that you have an uncomplicated pregnancy with a healthy baby boy in your womb. I cannot explain it, nor can he, but the problem is just not there. About the only way for it to be explained is that the sonogram across town was inconclusive, but I've never heard of that happening to get the results they did. I just don't get it.

"Anyway, he and I agree that you should be treated as a high-risk pregnancy for the balance of your term. I treat high-risk and he does not, so your former doctor is in agreement that you should remain a patient in our office. We will be watching you closely and doing weekly sonograms.

"Since I'm your physician now, I am ordering you to go home and relax and enjoy your pregnancy. Dad, your wife has had a difficult afternoon. I think she deserves special attention from you at home tonight. Stop at the desk and they'll schedule you for another appointment next week. If you need me please call me anytime."

The doctor left the room, shutting the door behind him for Becky to get dressed. Instead, she and Sam hugged each other and sobbed until they both were shaking. Sam turned then to give his wife that special attention the doctor had ordered, as he prayed and thanked God for the miracle healing of his unborn son.

Becky was dressed and her next appointment made before she and Sam stepped into the waiting room to discover the two friends with them, heads bowed, praying to God to spare the life of an unborn child. Both looked up to see a jubilant couple walking into that waiting room. Sam explained everything that happened. Well actually he explained nothing that happened, because God did it all behind the scenes. That Ford van headed back east was filled with jubilation and praise to God.

Like so many other people have done, Doug, a closet Christian, told himself, "Whatever those people have from Fellowship Church, Susan and I need it in our lives."

When the men got out of Becky's van to get their cars back at the first doctor's office, Sam did not know what to say. How can you possibly thank someone for saving the life of your unborn son? Actually neither man was expecting any thanks. Both were highly honored to be used by God to carry out His work and His purpose.

None of the Sullivan children ever knew how close their unborn brother had come to being aborted. Someday, when they are older, no doubt they will be told. The kids did notice that night their parents were praising God more than they had ever seen in their brief Christian lives.

As the doctor said, Becky had an uncomplicated pregnancy and a few months later gave birth to the prettiest little boy you have ever seen.

Sibling rivalry? The term was not even known at the Sullivan home. Rusty won a place in the heart of his brothers and sister the moment they saw him. The only disagreement over having a new baby in the house was whose turn it was to take care of him. Even young Ryan, seven years old, thought he was big enough to change his brother's diapers.

Kids grow up faster than we realize and before long Rusty was crawling around that same living room that once held his daddy's mountain of personal effects being returned home after satan's attack on this family. That did not work, so the evil one went after an unborn child in yet another effort to bring disruption to a Christian home. That did not work either, because a child had parents who knew the value of prayer.

One day, just as Rusty was starting to crawl, his daddy stopped at a toy store on the way home. He bought his son the first toy vehicle of his life. For the next few years, at different times in his growth, you could find Rusty on the living room floor playing with his toy tow truck.

Chapter 27

God's Pyramid Plan

Most of us, at one time or another have had a friend approach us offering a business opportunity that sounds too good to be true. Investing little money, we are going to have a great return, as we offer other people that same opportunity. Somehow those plans never work out as promised. We end up a few dollars shorter and wiser because of the scheme.

God's plan for marriage restoration, the hope of family restoration, works in much the same way. Only with God's pyramid plan, can you see the results. Yes, when you are praying and standing for a prodigal spouse you're making quite an investment, not of money, but of your life, in anticipation of God restoring your home. Once that happens, your marriage will be the basis upon which other marriages are also restored, as others witness what happened to you and hear the good news that God heals hurting marriages.

The story of the restoration of the marriage of Sam and Becky Sullivan is not complete until you hear about Russ Mortenson, the unemployed IT guy who led Sam to the Lord under a tree one Saturday afternoon, with car wax on his hands.

"Uncle Russ" became a frequently invited guest to the Sullivan home. The now four Sullivan kids adored him and he adored them, but his namesake, Rusty, had a special place in Russ' heart.

Sam had admired his roommate and looked up to him as a Christian. In truth, Russ was only a few steps ahead of Sam in his walk with Christ. After all, you only have to be one step ahead to meet someone anywhere. What matters is not how far ahead you are, but that you are going in the right direction and Russ certainly was.

God's Way Hosting, Mr. Dunnigan's dream of an all-Christian web hosting service, headed up by Russ, was flourishing. In fact, the marketing department and bean counters at Dunnigan Enterprises had warned Mr. Dunnigan they sensed the growth was too fast to be healthy. Nevertheless, John Dunnigan had to continue to promote the new company.

Could anything ever grow too fast if God is doing it? Consider that little boy on a hillside with his loaves and fishes. Did some accountant tug on the sleeve of Jesus and say, "Now don't provide more than we can distribute." Hardly. When Jesus is at work, man cannot restrict. Jesus was obviously at work helping Russ to build an all-Christian web hosting company.

The truth was that about as much work was being turned down as was being accepted. The criteria for coming on board with *GodsWay.com* was stringent. The service customers were receiving was above anything else available, but before being accepted, web sites were gone over with a fine tooth comb. If there was something even mildly offensive, concealed on a page deep within the site, Russ' staff would find it.

Mr. Dunnigan spared no expense in establishing this venture and it showed. Their sales department was bombarded with calls and email every day of the week. As you can imagine, John Dunnigan was thrilled with the results of his Christian venture.

Before long, *GodsWay.com* occupied an entire floor in

the bank building. Many days, when work permitted, Sam and Russ had lunch together in the bank cafeteria. No need to say that these two executives were not bashful about openly praying before their meal.

Mr. Dunnigan had another idea that he had emailed both Sam and Russ about. He would like to see if there was an interest in a Friday noon time Bible study for the entire building. The memo stated how careful they would have to be so that no one could accuse them of proselytizing, nor pressuring coworkers to attend. From the beginning it was Mr. Dunnigan's idea that he would personally pay for providing lunch for all who attended.

Ten days later, Sam and Russ sat in a small conference room with opened Bibles. Lunch trays from the cafeteria paid for by Mr. Dunnigan were brought in and set before them. The two men had a blessed time with the Lord praying for many things, including the salvation of everyone who worked in that building.

Even though a carefully worded memo had gone out inviting people to attend, only Sam and Russ came to Bible study that second week. Once again they prayed and once again they had their lunch provided for them.

On the third Friday, John Dunnigan was in town and joined the two men for Bible study and lunch. Someone from the cafeteria told a co-worker that Dunnigan must pick his fair-haired boys from those who attended. Even though only two employees attended, they both were in high positions.

That Friday a server on the cafeteria line casually mentioned to one person about Dunnigan having lunch with the men at Friday Bible studies. As you can imagine, that rumor spread throughout the building. The following Friday,

Sam and Russ were thrilled to have 37 people at Bible study with them. At the end, Sam overheard one man ask another, "Where is Dunnigan? I thought he came here to pick his execs."

Bible study attendance went up and down like the Dow Jones. A nucleus of men and women who love the Lord began to form. That nucleus, praise God, was ever expanding. Many bank and Dunnigan Enterprises employees gave their hearts to Jesus at those Friday meetings.

The Bible study also saw people walk through the door who did not have much money and were attending only for the free lunch. A few of these people, looking for only a free lunch even gave their hearts to Christ.

Mr. Dunnigan once said, "A storefront rescue mission offers a meal to get the 'down-and-outers' inside to hear the Gospel. We must be a rescue mission for the 'up-and-outers,' also giving them a free meal to hear the Gospel. Over time, Mr. Dunnigan had the lunch he served the Bible study attendees increased from soup and sandwiches to an entrée, to an elegant meal. The food at Bible study became the talk of the building, as did the weeks that John Dunnigan attended without notice and prayed with his employees. What a godly example of a Christian employer.

The new business was doing well when Russ was copied on an email from Mr. Dunnigan to Dunnigan Enterprises' marketing department. He was asking that an event with a Christian theme be planned locally to introduce *GodsWay.com* to the Fort Lauderdale community. John Dunnigan was soliciting ideas for an event.

Russ knew instantly what he would like to see the company do. His half brother, Mitch, was a bus driver for a

Christian singing group called *Reclaimed* out of Kentucky. Russ did not hear from Mitch often. In fact, it had been over a year since their last contact, but Mitch used to always write to Russ about wanting the group to come to South Florida so that he could renew his relationship with his half brother.

Since the letters in the past had been Christ-centered and Russ was still lost, he thought the letters to be offensive and usually only skimmed the text before throwing them out. Russ made a mental note, that regardless of any event, he still needed to rebuild his relationship with Mitch. Russ knew that Mitch must have been praying for him for years and he needed to know that Russ was now a new man.

Russ replied to the email without delay, giving his suggestion for the event that his employer desired to present to the community. He prayed that his suggestion might come to fruition so that his half brother could see face-to-face, not that Russ was successful in his career, but that he was a new man in Christ.

After a series of meetings and emails, not all of which were enthusiastic, with the secular marketing department hesitant to become involved in a Christian event, the group *Reclaimed* was booked for an upcoming Saturday night, about four months ahead, and the old War Memorial Auditorium was rented for the evening.

The marketing department was handling the details. Every few days Russ would receive an email from them, asking a question or giving him an update. Russ also received an email from his stepbrother, Mitch, who had seen Fort Lauderdale on the travel schedule for *Reclaimed.* Mitch was inviting Russ to come and hear the group. He had no idea that Russ was the person responsible for his music group being invited to Fort Lauderdale.

Russ, being the kind of guy he was, decided not to reply to Mitch's email. He knew the guy would be thrilled that he had become a Christian.

About 280 miles north of Fort Lauderdale, in Gainesville, Florida, the mail had just arrived at the home of a retired couple, Bill and Paula Brown. Bill was thumbing through a Christian magazine that he had received.

"Babe," Bill Brown called out to his wife, "that singing group that does so many of the old songs, I think their name is *Reclaimed*, is coming to Lauderdale on Saturday night. You've been wanting to hear them, so what do you think of us asking Lori to drive us down there? It would be good for her to have a change of scenery also. Would you pray about it?"

The very mention of the word "Lauderdale" was enough to get Paula Brown started on a monologue that her husband had heard countless times in the past year.

"Lauderdale! I can't hear anything about Lauderdale without thinking about that bum Russell that our Lori married. I told her when they were dating she was going to be unequally yoked. I reminded her time and time again that he came from a bad family, full of divorce and no one could hold down a job. He ran around Gainesville looking like a bum and pretending to be some kind of computer guy. Lori needs to go ahead and get some guts and divorce the loser."

"Now, we know that's Lori's decision and not ours. We have asked her to pray about it, right?" Bill Brown consoled his wife with the same words he had used a couple dozen times when she had gotten so upset with her daughter's failed marriage. "What do you say? Let's plan a weekend away with Lori and go hear that group."

“I guess it’s safe to go to Lauderdale. If whatever we are attending has the word Christian anywhere around it, it’s a sure bet our computer genius will not be sitting in the audience that night,” Paula Brown said with resolve.

Paula, you are correct. That “computer genius,” as you call your son-in-law will not be “sitting in the audience.” He will be backstage hosting the event. My dear lady, you are in for a shock!

Since her separation Lori had been living with her parents while she worked at a Gainesville law firm. That evening her parents asked her to drive them to Lauderdale on an upcoming Saturday night.

“You might as well go with us,” her mother scolded. “You should be going out on a Saturday night date, but instead you sit at home, pining away, and waiting for God knows what to happen. You’re not getting any younger and God has someone else for you, but you will not find him while you are sitting in front of the television every night.”

That was one of the many times when Lori wished she could afford her own apartment. How she loved her parents, but they just would not let her live her own life. Her mom was right, she had nothing to do that weekend, nothing at all, apart from church, so she might as well drive them down to Fort Lauderdale.

Lori’s first thought when she heard about the trip to Fort Lauderdale was about her husband, Russ. Since they had no children, and since she had not been to court requesting alimony, there was really no need for contact between the estranged couple.

About a year before, Lori had heard that her husband had

lost yet another job in Fort Lauderdale. He was surviving on part-time jobs and help from friends. Even if he was a "loser" as everyone insisted on reminding her, Russ was still her husband. Why could people, starting with her parents, not understand that?

On the Saturday of the Fort Lauderdale concert, Lori left Gainesville at 9 A.M. to drive her parents south. They planned to stay overnight and to attend church somewhere in Fort Lauderdale on Sunday and then drive home late Sunday.

Being up in years just a bit, Lori's parents did not like to drive fast, so Lori had the cruise control set just a bit under 70 miles an hour. It was a beautiful day to travel, and Lori's mother had not mentioned Russ or the divorce since they left home. Lori was fearful that because they were going to Fort Lauderdale, although to a place where Russ would never be, her mother would be reminded of what this "loser" had done to her daughter.

"Lord," Lori silently prayed as she drove, "I do not know how You could do it, but while we are down there, would you please allow me see Russ? Father God, you know how much I love him and how much I want to be with him, but there seems to be so many obstacles. I love you, Jesus, and I ask You for just a glimpse of my husband, Amen." Even though that was her prayer, Lori could not imagine how she would ever see her husband in an area with a population of two million people.

The Browns were just south of Micanopy, on the way to Ocala. Traffic was extremely light on I-75. Lori glanced at her outside mirror to see a big bus about to pass them. The speed of the bus was just a bit faster than the speed they were going, so the bus was about to overtake them slowly.

Looking back into her outside mirror, Lori thought, "I must be thinking about my husband too much because that bus driver looks so much like Russ."

Lori's thoughts were interrupted by her mother's exclamation, "Look! *Reclaimed*!" On the side of the huge burgundy and white bus, now directly even with their car, was the word *Reclaimed*. "That's them! That's who we are going to hear tonight!"

As the bus slowly passed them, underneath the Kentucky license plate was a second one. It read "God Heals Hurting Marriages." In the adjacent license plate holder was a plate reading "Prodigals Do Come Home." On the opposite side of the rear of the bus was a newer looking sign with only two words: "Forgive Them."

Even though Lori could not say a word to her parents, she thought it rather odd that just as she was praying, asking God to give her a glimpse of her husband, the bus carrying the group they were going to hear slowly passed them. Lori would have thought it more than "odd" if she knew that in the back cabin of that bus, at that very moment, were Dec and Tony Taylor. This couple had a restored marriage and traveled the nation declaring through song God's way of healing marriages. At the same time as they passed Lori, they were having morning devotions as a couple, asking God to send hurting, separated, and even divorced couples in Fort Lauderdale that night to their concert.

As the bus became smaller and smaller as it pulled ahead, Lori sensed a twinge of hope in her spirit. She could not say a word to her parents, or she might have been walking back to Gainesville, but within her heart of hearts, Lori sensed something good was about to happen.

Once the Browns arrived in Fort Lauderdale, they checked into their hotel and went to dinner. They then headed to the War Memorial Auditorium to arrive early to beat the crowd and to get good seats.

As the three Browns were walking into War Memorial Auditorium, unbeknownst to them, a husband and son-in-law were entertaining the family preparing to minister that night.

Russ was at War Memorial when the bus pulled in. First out of the door, almost as soon as the bus stopped rolling, was Mitch. While on the road, Tony Taylor had commented about Russ Mortenson being their contact person. Mitch thought that his half brother was still lost and tearing up letters.

The reconciliation between those two guys that took place, amidst a big hug, seconds after the bus door opened, was to set the theme for that entire night.

As the bus was unloaded, Russ first met Tony and Dee Taylor. Russ and Tony could have almost passed for brothers. Both were tall guys with outgoing personalities.

"Russ, do you have any relatives in Kentucky?" Dee joked with him, "You and my husband must have fallen out of the same family tree. It looks like we're in for a long night."

"Don't know about that, but we're in for a blessed night," Tony corrected.

Russ learned that Tony was at one time addicted to pornography. He and his wife had separated and were on the way to divorce when God spoke to him. Two books have been written about the Taylor family's transition from the divorce court to full-time traveling music ministry. Tony and

Dee came out of the bus with signed copies of "*A Day of Freedom*" and "*Pulpits in the Marketplace*" so that Russ, as their host, could learn more about this family group named *Reclaimed.*

Next out of the bus came John, the Taylor's son. As much as his wife Cindy wanted to be in on this quick trip to South Florida, both of the twins were sick with colds and she stayed home.

The Taylor's daughter, Debbie, seemed shy and reserved yet Russ could tell she was a real sweetheart. Just to hear her talk with her West Kentucky accent, Russ wanted to hear her sing.

And then there was Charlie, a shorter, round-faced young man who had been adopted into the road version of this singing family.

As the guys opened luggage bay doors and began to unload equipment to set up for the evening, Dee introduced Russ to ten-year-old Kyle. He was the son of church friends back in Paducah and thought it would be so cool to ride the bus for a weekend and to be able to tell his school friends that he was in Fort Lauderdale on Saturday.

Dee explained, "Kyle is our little Bible expert. He likes to be asked Bible questions. I suspect he knows more Bible than me."

Squaring off with Russ, towering about three feet over him, Kyle challenged, "Go ahead and ask me a question about the Bible, anything." Kyle stood in front of Russ like a wild West gunslinger, just daring Russ to stump him with a Bible question.

Russ came prepared for many responsibilities at the concert that Saturday night, but Bible quizzing was not one of them. Saying the first thing that came to his mind, Russ asked, "Who let animals on the ark?"

"Come on, that's too easy. Ask a hard question," the pint-sized Bible gunslinger fired back.

"All right," Russ said, pausing to think up a question. "What is the fifth book of the Bib..."

"Deuteronomy," Kyle fired back, before Russ even had the question all the way delivered.

Russ suddenly remembered something else that needed his attention.

While Russ was being defeated at Bible questions by a ten year old in the back of War Memorial, the three Browns were walking through the ticket gate into the auditorium. They were handed a program that had been professionally prepared for the evening. None of them looked at their program until they had found the seats they wanted, in the center section about five rows from the front. Once all three people were settled into their seats, Lori's mother was the first to open her program.

"OH MY!" was all she could get out. At first her husband thought she was having a heart attack as she raised her hand over her mouth and the blood drained from her face. She was speechless. All she could do was point at something inside her program. Bill Brown looked over to see what was there to cause such a reaction in his life. He saw a studio photo of his "loser" son-in-law. The man they said was sloppy and a loser, from a bad family, had his name and title underneath the photo. "Russell Mortenson, Vice President,

God's Way Hosting." Below that was printed, "Welcome to *A Night of Music God's Way*" followed by Russ' personal welcome and introduction to *God's Way Hosting.* At the bottom of the page was Russ' printed signature.

The three Browns looked like dominoes falling, as first mom, then dad, and finally Lori discovered what was inside that program. None of them spoke. None of them could believe that Lori's husband, the very man they wanted not to see, was their host this evening and responsible for everything taking place around them.

Many times in this story, the word shocked has been used, because being shocked by what God is doing in the restoration of one more marriage is part of the process. I can tell you that no other shocked scenario rated as high on the Shock-0-Meter as did what happened to the Browns that Saturday night. They were all shocked and stunned.

Fortunately the crowd coming into the auditorium was predictably noisy, which drowned out a lot of the things said by the Brown trio that no one needed to hear. Mother was still certain that Russ was a loser. "Maybe he does some computer things for them and they just paid him to use his name and picture."

Yes, Mom, you are exactly right. He does 'do some computer thing for them.' He runs an ever expanding Christian Web hosting company. You are also right that they paid him to use his name and picture. In fact, what they paid him to use his name and picture is called a salary and, even though low, it is a six digit number. Please remember that your son-in-law is also receiving some healthy performance bonuses for making a company grow. Mom, you need to let go of the past, and realize what God has done.

If you could have had a conversation with Pauline Brown, she probably would have asked you if God did all this just for the sake of the restoration of one marriage, her daughter's. "We do not know why God does what He does, but we do know that He always has the best interests of His children, his obedient children, at heart. Mom, God will never fail us."

The chatter between Lori Mortenson and her parents was still going on, attempting to figure out what had happened to Russ, until the lights went down, and a voice boomed through the speakers.

"Ladies and gentlemen, we welcome you to "*A Night of Music God's Way*." Here is your host, Russell Mortenson, vice president of *God's Way Hosting*."

With that Lori did more than get a glimpse of her husband, as she had asked God on the way down. Russ walked onto the stage looking like the executive that he had become. He was wearing an expensive suit and his grooming was immaculate. He still walked in that same lanky way and still wore the big Russ smile. As he picked up a microphone, Lori knew God had much more for her than what she had prayed for while driving her parents down.

Even though Russ was successful, very successful, in a position that still seemed new to him, Russ still lived in the same cracker box apartment that he had shared with Sam. "It's all I need, so why do I want to waste money before Lori comes home? Man, once she does I'm going to get her a nice place to live."

Russ was still the same old guy, attending Bible study with his brothers from church, faithful in his attendance at the noon service every Sunday and Wednesday evening. Russ was growing as a soul winner. Russ was just as faithful tithing to his church now as he had been when he was living on a very short shoestring.

There was a nicer car parked in space 111, right there by the tree where Sam had been saved. About one Saturday afternoon a month, Russ could be found out there waxing his company car.

Do you recall someone at church handing Russ an envelope with the exact amount of cash inside that he needed to get back his car? Russ never knew who that came from, but these days there was a box of plain envelopes sitting on the kitchen table next to Lori's picture. Just about weekly Russ would write the name of someone with a financial need on an envelope and put cash inside. He seldom handed these over at church directly, but many times he would point out an individual to an usher, saying, "Brother, could you hand this to the guy over there for me, but don't say where it came from."

What Russ was doing is exactly how standing and praying for marriage restoration God's way works. At one point when you were in need, someone handed you an envelope of truth that God does heal hurting marriages. Once you become rich in the truths of God's promises, you have a responsibility to pass an envelope of hope for troubled marriages along to others.

No, this is not after your marriage is restored, your spouse is home and everyone is serving the Lord. Just as Russ was still alone but blessing others, you need to be doing the same. Do you have any idea of the people who are watching you to see how you handle your present marriage crisis? You are a silent example to people not only at church, but at work, in your own family and your spouse's family as well.

Each time people in your circle of influence see you, are you handing out beat up empty envelopes of hopelessness, despair and defeat, being presented by a person who is unraveling, or are you passing out envelopes filled with hope for their problems?

Let's take a side trip and look at Sally and Susie. Although they do not know one another, both have similar circumstances. Their husbands have forsaken them for someone else. Both women have to count every penny. Both get discouraged, and both will tell you they are standing and praying for marriage restoration.

On the left side of the church Sally walks in. She is not dressed fancy, but she has let God know that she made an effort to come into His presence at that worship service. She is not dressed to attract the attention of women or men, but to attract the attention of her Creator. She has an envelope with her tithe, be it ever so small, to give to her church that day. Sally wears that glow that comes not from a specific brand of cosmetic, but from a close personal day by day walk with Jesus. When a man takes the seat next to her, Sally moves very obviously one seat to the right. At that service she sings the songs, taking the meaning of words to her heart. During the sermon, she has her Bible open, taking notes, and highlighting Scripture. After the service on her way to the parking lot, she passes Sister Busybody who asks about Sally's absent husband. Sally does not give the dear sister details, but requests she continue to pray for her prodigal.

At that same service, Susie walks in and takes a seat on the right side. Since she is going through such a mess she knows God would not expect her to waste energy getting fixed up for church. She did give thought to what she should wear that would make men take a second look. She brings no tithe envelope, because after all, the electric bill is due this week. Susie is isolated from the people around her. She cannot even force herself to smile. During praise and worship, she does not sing, but reflects on all of her many problems. The most uplifting part of the service is when a man takes the seat next to her. She does not have a Bible. During the sermon she is not listening, but making notes on things to tell her attorney. Susie does look around a bit, envious of other women who have a husband with them. Susie also encounters Sister Busybody who asks about her husband. Susie takes the opportunity to unload all the confidential details and all the rumors that she has heard in recent days. After all, God would want her to talk to someone. Sister Busybody is soon on her way to share all that she has just heard with anyone who will listen, under the guise of a prayer request. The dear sister forgot that Sally had requested prayer for her husband.

Which woman is passing on hope to others? After two prodigals come home, which one do you suppose would have the easiest time assimilating back into the church? One for whom prayer had been requested or one whose abandoned spouse had shared all?

That Saturday night at War Memorial Sally stood out. She was the woman, dressed up, with a glow on her face and a Bible in her lap. Did Susie, the second woman, blend into the crowd somewhere? No, she was not there because she was having coffee with a man who was "just a friend."

If those two women, who both claim to be praying for their prodigal to come home, should coincidentally run into their husbands on that Saturday night, who added and who deducted from what God wanted to do for their family?

Back on the stage, Russ was making introductions. One would think he had been doing this all of his life. In truth, God was blessing one of His faithful servants by putting him in a position, and helping him to do something far above his training and natural ability.

Russ successfully accomplished the purpose of the night in introducing *God's Way Hosting.* He introduced Mr. and Mrs. Dunnigan, sitting front row center. He also introduced the Sullivans, and explained in two short sentences about Sam being the first person he ever led to the Lord, and about their marriage being restored by God.

The Browns were shocked when the son-in-law they despised prayed in an auditorium filled with people. It was obvious to them, this prayer had been written not on his hand, as some might do in this situation, but had been written on his heart. Lori was thrilled, but not surprised, to hear her husband pray. She had been praying for him since the day they separated that he would somehow become a mighty man of God. It was evident that night by what she saw on a stage that he had.

Then came the introduction of the people everyone had come to hear, Tony and Dee Taylor and *Reclaimed.*

As the Taylors took the stage, Russ walked to the front row of seats and sat next to the Dunnigans. As you can imagine Lori had been watching every move her husband made, and hanging on his every word. She wondered who should have been sitting in that seat next to her husband in that coveted front row. As Russ sat down, a short man with red hair behind him gave him a hug across both shoulders, as if to say "Great job."

Sitting next to the man in the second row was a woman

Lori assumed to be his wife, along with three children. Lori listened to the Taylors, but she watched her husband. It was evident from the back-and-forth between Russ, the family behind him and the Dunnigans that they were close. Lori could not imagine how Russ was in such a position.

Mr. and Mrs. Brown's emotions were passing from shock to disbelief. Bill Brown thought that perhaps Russ had a twin brother they had never heard about. Paula Brown was embarrassed. All the time she had been saying humiliating things about Russ, he was obviously busy building a successful life as a Christian executive.

Dee had been accurate that afternoon standing by the bus when she had compared Russ and her husband Tony, being so much alike. Both men were not skilled communicators, but just down to earth "what you see is what you get" guys who were very transparent about what they believed. After these likable hillbillies from Paducah, Kentucky sang their first three "coming on" songs, Tony introduced his family and their friends. By the time he was done you had the feeling that you had known these folksy characters for years. That's one of the two traits that set *Reclaimed* apart from most every other group in concert that night. The second trait was their sincere love for the Lord and what He could do, especially for a hurting marriage.

The people at War Memorial that Saturday night loved Tony and Dee's back-and-forth chatter, of which there was much. There was also great music and a lot of talk about marriage, making it work, and about restoration after a marriage that seemed not to work.

In between two songs Tony introduced Kyle, the ten-year-old church friend who had come with them. Kyle was sitting in the front row next to the open seat beside Russ.

Tony explained to the audience how Kyle liked to answer Bible questions. To demonstrate, Tony asked a question about a verse in the Ten Commandments. He did not want to embarrass the kid, so Tony tossed Kyle a slow ball, a question he could not get wrong.

Kyle answered in a voice too deep for most ten-year olds, and a volume that could be heard all over that auditorium.

"Come on, that's too easy. Don't you know any hard questions?"

The audience exploded in applause and laughter. Kyle, a kid who was not afraid of any situation, stood up, turned around and took a bow.

Connie Sullivan, also 10 years old, was sitting with her family directly behind Kyle. She had just found the first boy that she liked.

The Browns were apprehensive about what was about to happen that night. Lori was not. She watched every move of the back of her husband's head for an entire hour.

During the intermission, many people visited the concession stand or stood up and walked around. Lori stayed in her seat, with her eyes following her husband's every move. Her mother was not encouraging. "Now honey, I don't want you getting your hopes up. We just do not know the whole story yet."

Yes, Lori Mortenson knew the whole story. She was married to a covenant husband. True, she did marry a nonbeliever and they were unequally yoked, but in response to her prayers, and no doubt the prayers of many others, God had saved her husband. Just as the name of the group there tonight, God had reclaimed His prodigal son. Lori sensed that God was also about to reclaim a marriage, even if it meant over the objections of her domineering mother and a go-along-with-the-flow father.

The house lights dimmed and Russ took the stage once again. He gave the commercial the marketing department had written for him, but it did not come out at all like the experts had intended. It came across more like a guy you just met, but whose sincerity you can easily see. It sounded as if he were explaining an all Christian web hosting service that he had been hired to build and which operated from first-class servers sitting in the corner of his bedroom.

The Dunnigan marketing people who were listening cringed at their polished presentation being butchered by their standards, but being blessed by God's standards. Opinions changed when they saw the crowd around the booth in the lobby after the concert. By the way, in the week following that evening, *God's Way Hosting* had more new subscribers than in any week prior. Their web site *http://GodsWay.com* had over a million visitors that month.

On that stage, Russ had finished presenting the prepared remarks and had even added some of his own, yet the group had not returned to the stage. He had to come up with a way to fill some time real quick. Looking down at the front row, he saw Kyle, the Bible kid, sitting there and smirking at him. "Kyle, come up here."

While an usher was directing Kyle to the stairs onto the stage Russ explained, "Young Kyle and I were in the midst of something this afternoon we did not finish." By then, Kyle was standing beside Russ. You might expect a kid thrust into that situation to face the audience and just stare at them. Instead, Kyle stood at right angles to the audience, ready for another Bible Q & A shoot-out with Russ.

"I did not get to finish asking Kyle Bible questions earlier, so buddy, let's do it now," Russ challenged.

Kyle had picked up a microphone and said, "Go on. Give me the best you've got." Russ had incorrectly assumed that the youngster would be as frightened as he had been when he had first stepped on the stage that night. Instead, Russ was afraid that he was about to shoot himself in the foot.

Sure enough, for every Bible question Russ came up with, Kyle had the answer. It was Russ, not Kyle who froze. When Russ paused, someone in one of the front rows of the audience asked a question from the Bible. Kyle answered and added, "Anybody else?"

People roared with laughter at this kid who not only knew so much about the Bible, but who had the confidence at 10 years old to challenge an auditorium full of people. Soon questions were being shouted from different parts of that crowd. Yes, Kyle missed a few, but for the most part he answered every question.

Russ was getting concerned because the group had not returned to the stage. What he did not know is that they were ready and had walked back in to see what was happening and had stood along the sides of the building until these two characters had finished.

Lori sat there watching her husband. In her mind she could imagine Russ interacting with their children, yet unborn, just as he was doing with Kyle. If she ever had a doubt about God's call on her life to be a Christian wife and mother, it was dissolved right then.

People were still returning to their seats from intermission and with all the laughter and questions being shouted, two things happened that most people did not even notice. Dee had dispatched Mitch to the bus to get the camera and take pictures of Kyle on the stage.

That was minor compared to the second event taking place at the same time. Lori excused herself across half a row of people to get to the aisle. Her parents had assumed that she was going to the ladies' room. Instead, when she reached the aisle, Lori turned not toward the back of the auditorium, but to the front. She walked straight to the empty seat next to where her husband Russ would soon return.

Reclaimed had returned to the stage. Tony asked for applause for the two guys who had just spontaneously blessed the audience. Kyle, still holding the microphone deepened his voice, and did his Elvis impersonation saying, "Thank you, thank you very much." The audience went wild, but it was mild compared to what would happen in about two minutes. Russ and Kyle walked off the stage together with Russ' long arm around Kyle's shoulder.

Speaking of shoulders, as soon as Lori sat down, she felt a tap on her left shoulder. "Excuse me, but that seat is saved for someone," the woman in the second row declared.

Lori turned all the way around said, "I think it was saved for me."

Becky Sullivan realized she was face to face with Russ' wife, whose photo sat on their kitchen table.

Have you ever been in a large auditorium where there was a major disruption? That pretty well explains what happened that night at 9:37 P.M. in War Memorial

Auditorium. The house lights were down so you really could not see everything, except for illumination from the stage lighting. This all happened just as Russ and Kyle were headed down the stairs, coming off the stage. It was not just Becky's bloodcurdling scream that brought things to a halt, but a combination of laughter and shrieks.

Russ' first thought of what happened was that he would be losing his job. That night, with so much planning and such expense to Dunnigan, had just collapsed. Russ quickly let go of Kyle's shoulder and looked toward the disruption. At first he thought that Becky was restraining a woman attempting to get up to the stage. From a distance they seemed to be hugging and jumping. Russ quickly headed for the disturbance to see if he could calm it down and maybe salvage the night. His reactions only made it much worse.

"It's Lori!" Russ almost shouted. "God brought her here! Praise the Lord! My prayers are answered! I knew God would do it!" With that, Russ pried Becky off of his wife and hugged her in his arms, oblivious to the thousands of people who were watching them.

Tony and Dee did not know the reason for the disruption, but they had seen enough sudden marriage restorations to recognize when God was moving and this was one of those times. *Reclaimed* went back to playing and singing softly as the scenario in the front row played out.

John Dunnigan had not planned to speak at all that evening, but he sensed being led to go to the stage and explain what was happening. John Dunnigan gave away a lot of family secrets, not about himself, but about others.

"I'm John Dunnigan, president of Dunnigan Enterprises. You might be wondering about the disturbance in the front row just now." When he began speaking, everyone who had been standing in the front took their seats, with Russ having a death grip on his wife's hand. Mr. Dunnigan continued to tell about Sam and Becky, about how their neighbors arranged for them to be at the same cottage for the same weekend. He even told about young Rusty, at home tonight with a babysitter. In fact, he probably told too much about how Rusty got his middle name.

Dunnigan related about the first time he met Russ and how God sent a man who shared his vision for a clean Christian Web hosting service. The president even told of how one of his officers, terminated by mistake, helped to repo Russ' car.

"That was all in the past and has been forgiven by the Blood of Jesus. Now these two men both have their wives and are working alongside me to bring you the finest, the purest web hosting. Sam is working with me to make our bank the finest in Broward County.

"I want to personally thank you for being our customers, or our potential customers. With God's help we will never disappoint you. Now, Tony Taylor, how about some more of that fine music from your family?" Dunnigan concluded.

There was a lot more of that music, but there was something else also. Mitch, the bus driver, was led to share how his marriage was restored when his wife showed up at a concert in Hannibal, Missouri, not expecting to see him there. Dee and Tony shared even more about their testimony of pornography attempting to steal her husband. Charlie shared about his marriage being healed.

Between the music and the testimonies, Mrs. Paula Brown was convicted of how wrong she had been to encourage her daughter's divorce. Paula asked God to forgive her for all the things she had said about Russ. Paula trampled on a few toes making her way to the aisle. She discreetly walked to the front and knelt down in front of her daughter and son-in-law.

“Please forgive me,” she tearfully began. “I have done so much wrong in all the things I said about you Russ, and Lori, I attempted to keep you away from your husband. I couldn't sit there any longer. Will you both please forgive me?”

“Mom, you are totally forgiven. Everything is new from right now and the past is behind us,” Russ said to his mother-in-law. With a motion like he was shooing the chickens away, Russ chased Kyle from the seat next to Lori so that she could sit with her mother.

“Come here, young man,” John Dunnigan said to Kyle. “I have a seat for you, right here on my knee.” Kyle listened to the final part of that Saturday night concert perched on the right knee of one of the most prominent people in Fort Lauderdale. Mrs. Dunnigan, sitting next to her husband, reached up and softly touched Kyle's back. Amidst all the happiness, this dear couple were grieving the fact that they never had a child that could be doing what Kyle was doing at that moment.

It’s difficult to say when that concert ended. Tony gave an invitation, inviting people who had never given their heart to Christ to do so. Many people responded. Following that, he invited couples with marriage problems to come to the front for prayer. After he prayed for them, Dee extended an invitation for men and women who were in the situation that she had been in, with a prodigal husband and unsure what to do, to come to the front. Scores of individual people responded and were prayed with.

When most concerts end, everyone heads for the door. On that night, people seemed to want to stay around the stage. Many were kneeling and praying.

What happened to Bill Brown, whose wife and daughter had moved to the front during one part of that invitation? Bill had gone to the front and taken his wife by the hand. Even though the Browns had been married almost 50 years, on that night he accepted the role that God had for him as spiritual head of the Brown family, a role that his wife joyfully relinquished on her knees. Afterward, he went to Russ to ask for his forgiveness and to officially welcome a son into their family.

Weeks prior, the Dunnigans had planned to entertain their guests, Russ and the Sullivan family, a group estimated to be about 30 people. Mrs. Dunnigan contacted different hotels looking for just the perfect place. The Taylors were headed back to Paducah as soon as they finished Saturday evening, so the Dunnigans wanted a place that would show their Paducah guests what Fort Lauderdale looked like.

You will not believe where they decided to have their event - in the large conference room on the top floor of the bank building. They considered asking the bank cafeteria staff to provide food, but instead they had it catered.

All three Sullivan kids were invited to ride on the bus to the bank, where bank security waited to escort them up the express elevator to the top floor and the conference room.

From a business standpoint, the night was far more successful than could ever have been anticipated and left the secular marketing people scratching their heads. The evening turned out being all about marriages, but there was a new relationship formed that night as well.

On the bus, on route to the bank building, Connie and Kyle developed a friendship that would last for years. None of the parents understood, yet these two kids had a brother and sister relationship. They exchanged frequent email, under the watchful eye of a parent. The words boyfriend or girlfriend were never used. All through their teen years they confided in one another. More than once Kyle hitched a ride on the bus known as "The Ark" when it was headed for Florida.

When the Sullivans would go on vacation, proximity to Paducah seemed to be Connie's criteria for her suggestion for a destination. For a few years, Kyle's parents, the Lockson's, vacationed in Fort Lauderdale to the delight of the two kids. All four parents suspected that some day a romance would rise from that friendship, but it never did.

Several years later, when Connie became serious about one young man, she and Kyle knew they could no longer be friends. It was a heartbreaking time, but they were in agreement that God had someone special to be their mates and an opposite sex friendship could harm their love for a spouse. All four parents were thankful for the true friends their kids had become.

High in that conference room Saturday night, Connie was walking around all four sides by the floor to ceiling windows, pointing out landmarks to Kyle. He had been told there would not be time to see the Atlantic Ocean, but his new friend Connie was able to show it to him. She pointed out Las Olas and told him the direction of Miami. They saw planes arriving and taking off from Fort Lauderdale-Hollywood International Airport. Mr. Dunnigan even came up with a pair of binoculars from somewhere for Kyle and Connie to use.

The Sullivan boys had never been up to that room before. They had a ball, between talking with the people from Kentucky, looking out those big windows and seeing what they could recognize and of course, teasing their sister about having a boyfriend.

If you needed Russ anytime after that concert, he would not have been hard to find. Just look for Lori and they would be together. Going into the evening, Tony Taylor said Russ Mortenson would be their host. By the time the reception was over, Russ was sitting with his wife and her parents, all four getting to know people they at one time disliked before the sun had set on that day.

Both security and caterers worked overtime that night because this night was too special to end. The Dunnigans sat by themselves, off to the side, for the better part of the reception.

"My dear," John Dunnigan softly told his wife, "all these years we have been thanking God for our material blessings, but asking Him why He never gave us a family. Just look around this room. God has indeed given us a family. Praise His Name."

It was almost midnight when Russ, as only Russ could do, got everyone's attention so they could pray together before heading home. His wife and his in-laws, had never stood prouder.

The caterer had been instructed to pack leftover food for the bus. All the way home they would be snacking on food such as shrimp cocktail and key lime pie, reminding them of Fort Lauderdale. The goodbyes were exchanged, and the idling bus was loaded to head back to Paducah.

The bus known as "The Ark" was northbound on the Florida Turnpike, nearing West Palm Beach. The guys were getting their bunks ready for the night and Debbie was in her small room. Dee and Tony were in their room in the very back of the bus. Tony took off his jacket and emptied the pockets.

"Don't lose the check from tonight," Dee cautioned. She knew her husband's propensity for talking when the honorarium check was given to him and then forgetting where he put it. "We really need that check because our schedule is super light." Dee concluded.

"God always provides," Tony reminded her. "I know we don't have money for payroll next week for us and the guys, but God has never failed us yet, has He?"

"If you want I can put tonight's check in my purse so we'll know where it is." Dee said.

Tony handed his wife the business check, folded in half, that Mr. Dunnigan had handed him at the reception. He had given it to Dee without looking at it. As Dee put the check in her purse, she glanced at it and discovered that it was for $5,000 more than the contracted price for the group's coming to Fort Lauderdale.

In the back compartment of an old bus bouncing up the Turnpike toward Kentucky, a husband and wife lay in each other's arms falling asleep. Before they did, they thanked God for the miracles in marriages that He had allowed them to witness that night. They prayed for safe travel, as well as for the new friends God had allowed them to make that evening. They prayed for their children and their grandchildren. They prayed for services at their church which would begin in just a few hours that they would be missing this week. They almost forgot to thank God for the financial provision He had made for their ministry. It wasn't that they were ungrateful, but so many other things and people were more important than money.

Russ and Lori had followed his wife's parents back to their hotel so Lori could get her suitcase and go home with her husband. The Dunnigans invited everyone to join them Sunday morning after church for brunch at the yacht club.

They were running late for church, so Lori and Russ went ahead to save seats. As they were putting bulletins on seats to save them for her parents, the Dunnigans , the Tomlinsons and of course Sam and Becky, Russ knew exactly the seat he needed. As Lori took her seat next to him, Russ whispered in her ear, "I've been saving that seat for you for 113 services and I am glad you are here."

After church, there came more goodbyes as Lori and her parents prepared to leave. Her plans were to go back to Gainesville and give two weeks notice at her job so she could move to Fort Lauderdale with her husband.

Mr. Dunnigan said to Lori, "You're going to be needing a job down here, so let me know what day you're going to start and we will have a position for you. I hired your husband at my home without knowing much about him, and that's worked out pretty well, so here I am hiring you at church just because you're married to a man I greatly respect."

Two things happened Monday morning that end our story. Lori gave her notice at the attorney's office. She told her boss about the weekend. Lori was a respected employee and they hated to see her go, but she was told she could leave immediately. On Friday she was back in Fort Lauderdale, leaving behind parents who hated to see her go, but who were rejoicing at her marriage being restored, to the glory of God.

On that same Monday morning, Mr. Dunnigan called in his secretary at the bank. "I need you to open up trust accounts for college educations for five great kids, four with the last name Sullivan and one named Kyle Lockson." That wise man had learned years before that he could not out-give God.

A complex story of marriage restoration, you say? It is not difficult for our mighty God. What He has done for the people in this story, He is wanting to do in every hurting marriage, if one spouse will pray and allow Him to work His will and His way. Praise God that prodigals do come home.

Epilog

Ten Years Later

Have you ever read a fiction story and wondered what happened to the characters? Let's take a look ten years ahead at the people from this story.

The Sullivans - Still living in the same Coral Ridge home. They are now preparing to celebrate their 25th wedding anniversary to the glory of God. All five members of the family know the Lord and are active in Fellowship Church. After Sam was made a vice president at the bank a couple years before, they had their home totally renovated. Even though their home was now a two-story and elegant, it was more than ever a place of prayer. If you have ever been in a situation like Sam and Becky were 10 years ago, be confident that there are a lot of couples just like them who are praying for you and your spouse every day.

Sam Sullivan - Sam, now middle-aged, still looks in the mirror at himself and prays every morning. God had given him a unique talent to minister to other men who were going through marriage problems. He is an elder at Fellowship Church and invaluable to the church in financial matters. Sam had been invited by his political party to run for the Florida Legislature, but he declined, fearing that he might win. If you ever visit his office, now even higher in a downtown Fort Lauderdale bank, please note the model tow truck displayed there. "That truck is my scar to remind me to never go back there again," Sam will tell you.

Becky Sullivan - Becky had found her calling in working with pregnant girls in a crisis pregnancy center. She puts in more hours each week than if she would be working full time. Some of the children Becky helped save from the abortionist are now eight and nine years old.

Grant Sullivan - Grant, 22, is graduating from Liberty University in Lynchburg, Virginia where he attended on a full scholarship for, of all things for a South Florida kid, ice hockey. After Sam had come home 10 years prior and began to spend time with his kids being a real dad, they discovered Grant's natural ability at ice hockey. Grant was sensing a call to foreign missions and had been accepted in Liberty's Missions program.

Connie Sullivan - Now 20 years old, Connie is the apple of her daddy's eye. She is in her second year of nursing at Broward Community College and still lives at home. There is a boyfriend in the picture who is the son of a church friend. Sam and Becky have talked often with Connie and her boyfriend about the permanence of marriage. If they do get married, they know it is for life. By the way, if you were to look in Connie's room today, hanging from her bulletin board are three pressed roses and a card, sent to her 10 years before.

Ryan Sullivan - Ryan, 17, will be graduating from high school soon. His long-term plans are to become a banker, just like his dad. Ryan is personality plus and is a witness for Christ at Mainlands Christian Academy where he attends school. Unlike his brother, the athlete, Ryan has an interest in drama. Sam and Becky would not be surprised if he were to become a Christian actor instead of a banker.

Russell Pierce Sullivan - Rusty, as he is known, is a nine year old replica of his dad at that age, red hair and all. He is a fourth grader at Mainlands Christian Academy who loves Jesus, his family, and soccer. Rusty will never have to endure having a parent being absent due to marital strife, as did his brothers and sister, because Jesus now leads the Sullivans. He was named after Russ, who led his dad to the Lord. There was a weekend in South Georgia, where both he and his middle name came from.

Sandy - Sandy, the nurse, is approaching retirement age. Sadly her search for Mr. Right has taken her through a string of men. She never realized that Jesus was the right Man for her.

Tony - The cook at Skyline Chili who first introduced Becky to someone who could tell her about both Jesus and marriage restoration rejoiced when Sam came home. Sam talked to Tony often about Jesus, but Tony always wanted to wait one more day before giving his life to Christ. Sadly, Tony continued to gain weight and work long hours and a few years ago dropped dead of a massive heart attack. No one knows if Tony knew Jesus. Although Sam passes Skyline twice a day coming and going to work, he has only been there once this year. He will tell you his heart doctor said to back off on the foods he enjoyed, but if you knew Sam's heart, you would know it breaks for Tony each time he sits at that counter.

The Tomlinsons - This couple was still the next-door neighbors to the Sullivans. Doug had retired and they spend a lot of time at that expanded cottage in South Georgia. Should you ever pass by, you would recognize it by the engraved wooden sign over the front door that reads "Fort Pierce."

Russ Mortenson - Russ, now 41 years old, was the once-unemployed IT guy who led Sam to the Lord and was the roommate who discipled him in the Christian faith. Russ is vice president of an extremely successful Christian web hosting company that he will one day own. He and his wife, Lori, are the parents of six year old twins, who are first graders at Mainlands Christian Academy. Russ still drives the ushers crazy at Fellowship Church. With Lori on one side, he insists on saving the seat on the other side of him for someone he has led to the Lord that week. If you were to attend the 12 noon service at Fellowship Church on a Sunday and tell any usher that the guy who had led you to Christ said he would be saving a seat for you, out of the 5,000 people at that service, they would take you to Russ.

Jerry - The repo guy who befriended Sam is still in that business and as hard as ever. Anita, his live-in companion of many years, left him years ago to go home to her own husband. Jerry says, "I have sworn off women." This man's salvation is high on Sam's personal prayer list. Jerry has refused every invitation from Sam to attend church. Every time Sam gets close to speaking about things eternal with Jerry, he always has another call and needs to hang up.

Kathy - Jerry's wife still lives in Alabama, near her elderly parents and continues to stand strong for the restoration of her marriage, as well as for Jerry to come to Christ. Kathy has become discouraged a few times, when satan has pulled out a big gun of circumstances, but God has given her victory each time. God has also given her victory over the calendar. Her focus is on matters eternal, not on how long she has been standing. Kathy is active in the marriage restoration group that she helped to establish at her church. Jerry and Kathy's son, Junior, is his Mom's number one prayer partner.

Junior - Jerry and Kathy's son, Junior, lives at home with his Mom. He is taking distance learning online Bible classes from a Christian college. Apples must not fall far from the tree, because Junior is working for a wrecker service which does repossessions. Junior's vision is to someday start a Christian repo service. God has already given him several opportunities to witness for Christ to people in financial trouble whose car he was about to tow away.

Jim Jackson - Jim was the youth pastor who had led Grant to the Lord on the first Sunday that Becky had taken her family to Fellowship Church. He is no longer on the staff at Fellowship Church, but is senior pastor at a burgeoning new church in Valdosta, Georgia. It was named Fellowship Church North. On any Sunday, you could have found any of a number of our friends from this story worshiping at that church.

Judge William Bahnsen - Serving his second term in the Florida legislature, where he has developed a reputation for being pro-family and pro-life. He won his seat by a landslide.

Kyle Lockson - Now age 20, Kyle is also attending Liberty University where he is majoring in Journalism, with a minor in Political Science. Kyle plans to become a conservative talk show host, but no one would be surprised to see him on the national political scene some day. If that happens, God will have one more man in Washington.

"Not If But When"

If you were ever to hear Tony and Dee Taylor and their group, *Reclaimed*, in concert, you would be certain to hear an original song that Dee wrote:

The question's not "if," but only a matter of "when,"
Our mighty God will come through and do it again.
He knows your heart as for a prodigal you pray.
All the forces of hell can't keep your mate away.

The question's not "if," but only a matter of "when,"
Standing for a prodigal mate seems strange to men.
"Get on with your life," most people really do say,
They don't know why for our mates we pray.

The question's not "if," but only a matter of "when,"
God will make us all a happy family in the end.
So, dear one, stand firm, do fast and do pray,
Waiting for your prodigal is God's best way.

The question's not "if," but only a matter of "when,"
A covenant spouse will turn from their life of sin.
What God has started He will finish to the end,
The question's not "if," but only a matter of "when."

- Dee Taylor

Meet The Steinkamps

Things were not always blissful for Bob and Charlyne. They separated several times and finally divorced in1985 after 19 years of marriage, and with three children. Two years later, in response to the prayers of a wife who had refused to give up on a prodigal husband, Bob and Charlyne were remarried, to the glory of God, who restored their marriage.

In 1989, the Lord led them in two ways that were to become the birth of Rejoice Marriage Ministries. Following a late night conversation Bob overheard in a hospital regarding divorce that day, he started to write his first book, *"Prodigals Do Come Home."* About the same time, Charlyne was led to approach their pastor regarding her burden to teach a Bible study for women standing for restoration of their marriage or for an unsaved spouse.

Since that time, Bob and Charlyne have written twenty books on marriage restoration. Their testimony was dramatized worldwide on ***Unshackled!*** from Pacific Garden Mission in Chicago. They have appeared on TBN and have been interviewed on radio and television, and had newspaper and magazine stories of their testimony. The Steinkamps also host both a daily and a weekly radio program of their own.

A Rejoice Bible study group that began with a handful of women in the Steinkamps' living room in 1989, now meets twice monthly with both men and women at rented facilities in Pompano Beach. Tens of thousands of Charlyne's teaching messages from those classes have been distributed worldwide on cassette and CD.

The second greatest accomplishment of Rejoice Marriage Ministries has been to witness couple after couple whose hopeless marriages have been restored, even after divorce. The greatest accomplishment of the Ministry has been to help untold scores of men and women discover a relationship with our Lord Jesus Christ.

The Steinkamps duplicated 60 copies of their first two-page newsletter in 1990. Today, thousands of subscribers around the world receive *Charlyne Cares*, a free daily email devotional written for hurting spouses. Rejoice Marriage Ministries also has several web sites, receiving thousands of visitors each week. Several thousand other people listen to *God Heals Hurting Marriages*, their daily five-minute radio program, also available online.

Following God's word for them to "Proclaim," Rejoice Marriage Ministries has rented highway billboards that read, in three-foot high letters, "There's Hope - God Heals Hurting Marriages."

In 2007, *Stop Divorce Radio* began, broadcasting good music and good news around the clock for hurting spouses.

Bob and Charlyne's books are written, and messages taped, to give encouragement to hurting spouses, not to be rule books. The only book you really need to see your marriage restored is the Bible.

You may be reading this book searching for something to help your marriage problems. The "something" you are seeking is really "someone," and His name is Jesus. Please contact us if Rejoice Marriage Ministries can help you discover the difference that the Lord can make in a fractured family. God Heals Hurting Families!

"My sheep listen to my voice; I know them, and they follow me. I give them eternal life, and they shall never perish; no one can snatch them out of my hand. My Father, who has given them to me, is greater than all; no one can snatch them out of my Father's hand. I and the Father are one." ***John 10:27-30***

Ten Sources of Help

Here are ten ways that Rejoice Marriage Ministries, Inc. can help to keep you encouraged and strong as you stand with God and pray for the restoration of your family.

Prayer - The number one source of help for your marriage is centered on prayer. While we have several prayer lists and an online Chapel, our goal is to teach you how to pray for your prodigal, for yourself and for your family.

The Bible - We strive to teach you how to get your answers from the Word of God. "Someone said," really should not carry much weight with what you do, but reading for yourself what God said brings you answers and direction that will *always* be 100% in alignment with God's will for you and for your family. Learn to turn to the Word.

Charlyne Cares - Seven days a week we send subscribers a daily devotional by that name. Always based on scripture, some days Charlyne teaches and other days she shares her heart. Subscribe for free from http://CharlyneCares.net

Stop Divorce Radio - We broadcast good music and Good News around the clock for men and women facing marriage problems. We strive to make programming prodigal-friendly and pray that prodigals find us by accident. Stop Divorce Radio often plays in the background of our own home - http://StopDivorceRadio.org

Stop Divorce Bookstore - Our online bookstore offers our books, along with marriage restoration teaching on both cassette and CD. Other items, such as front license plates are also available- http://StopDivorce.org

God Heals Hurting Marriages - Our five minute weekday audio vitamin for standers. If you will get into the habit of starting your day by listening, you will be amazed how often the program's subject will be exactly what you need to hear for that day - http://rejoiceministries.org/r.php?num=8le78

Fight For Your Marriage - A weekly 30 minute audio Bible study online. You will get a feel for what we do at Rejoice Pompano, where most of the teaching messages are recorded - http://rejoiceministries.org/r.php?num=stmb8

Rejoice Pompano - Standers in South Florida meet with us here in Pompano Beach on the first and third Monday evenings of each month for Bible study, prayer, support and fellowship. From time to time we also take Rejoice on the Road to other communities - http://RejoicePompano.org

Web Site - The Rejoice Marriage Ministries web site has over a thousand pages of helps, ranging from Q &A to audio and video to testimonies for the man or woman facing marriage interruption - http://RejoiceMinistries.org

Personal Contact - Every email is read and prayed for by a paid staff member and most are also reviewed by one or both of us. The one thing we cannot do is to give direct advice, telling you what you should or should not do. We might get it wrong, but if we teach you how to listen to God, He will always give you the right answers.

We have many other helps available for the man or woman who is seriously seeking marriage restoration God's way. We encourage you to take advantage of each one of them.

Rejoice Marriage Ministries, Inc.
Bob and Charlyne Steinkamp, Founders
Post Office Box 10548
Pompano Beach, Florida 33060 USA
http://rejoiceministries.org

The Greatest News

"That if you confess with your mouth, 'Jesus is Lord,' and believe in your heart that God raised him from the dead, you will be saved." ***Romans 10:9***

Many people in a hurting marriage have discovered that the first step in a healed marriage is to have a personal relationship with Jesus Christ. Our God and Creator is waiting to hear your prayer. Have you received Jesus Christ as Lord and Savior of your life? He will save you and be your Comforter and Counselor in the days ahead, regardless of the circumstances.

A Prayer For You

"Dear Jesus, I believe that You died for me and that You rose again on the third day. I confess to You that I am a sinner and that I need Your love and forgiveness. Come into my life, forgive me for my sins, and give me eternal life. I confess to You now that You are my Lord and Savior. Thank You for my salvation. Lord, show me Your will and Your way for my marriage. Mold me and make me to be the spouse I need to be for my spouse. Thank You for rebuilding my marriage. ***Amen.***"

Signed____

Date____

"Believe in the Lord Jesus, and you will be saved--
you and your household." ***Acts 16:31***

Notes On What God Has Shown Me About Saving A Seat In My Life For Someone Special

May the God of hope fill you with all joy and peace as you trust in him, so that you may overflow with hope by the power of the Holy Spirit. ***Romans 15:13***

Notes On What God Has Shown Me About Saving A Seat In My Life For Someone Special

May the God of hope fill you with all joy and peace as you trust in him, so that you may overflow with hope by the power of the Holy Spirit. ***Romans 15:13***

Notes On What God Has Shown Me About Saving A Seat In My Life For Someone Special

May the God of hope fill you with all joy and peace as you trust in him, so that you may overflow with hope by the power of the Holy Spirit. ***Romans 15:13***

Notes On What God Has Shown Me About Saving A Seat In My Life For Someone Special

May the God of hope fill you with all joy and peace as you trust in him, so that you may overflow with hope by the power of the Holy Spirit. ***Romans 15:13***

Notes On What God Has Shown Me About Saving A Seat In My Life For Someone Special

May the God of hope fill you with all joy and peace as you trust in him, so that you may overflow with hope by the power of the Holy Spirit. ***Romans 15:13***